# SOUNDS OF LANGUAGE

readers

Sounds of Children
    at Play on the Hill
Sounds Around the Mountain
Sounds of an Owly Night
Sounds of Home
Sounds of Numbers
Sounds Around the Clock
Sounds of a Powwow
Sounds of Laughter
Sounds After Dark
Sounds of the Storyteller
Sounds of Mystery
Sounds Around the Campfire

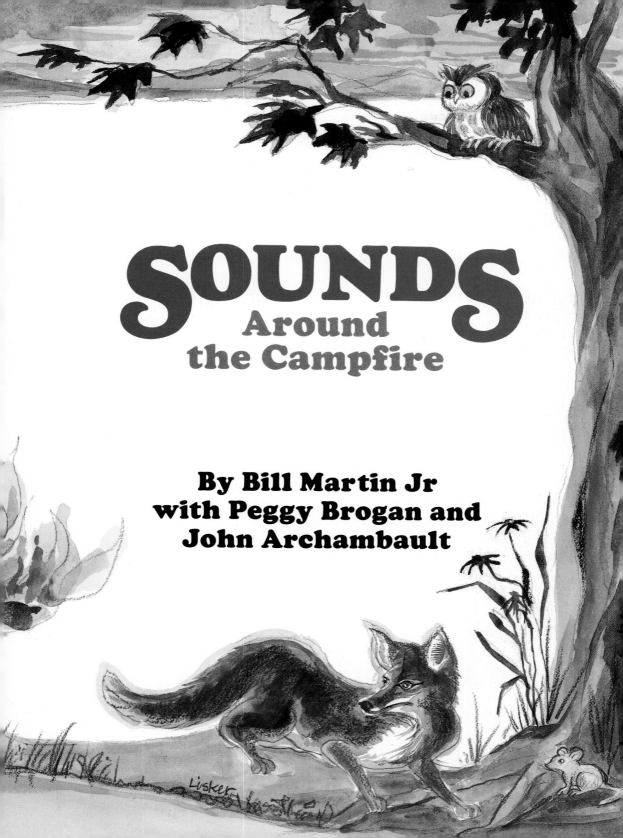

# SOUNDS
## Around the Campfire

**By Bill Martin Jr
with Peggy Brogan and
John Archambault**

# ACKNOWLEDGMENTS

Acknowledgment is made to Betty Jean Mitchell for permission to use her character Noodles © 1981.

Thanks to Linda Ross, Carol Misiaszek, and Donna Rodgers for their editorial and production assistance.

Every effort has been made to locate and secure permissions from the copyright holders for the selections used in this book. The publishers will be grateful if any omissions or errors are brought to their attention, so that they may be corrected.

Cover illustrations by Ted Rand.

Front illustrations by Sonia O. Lisker.

KNOTS ON A COUNTING ROPE by Bill Martin Jr and John Archambault. Illustrations by Ted Rand. Text copyright © 1966 and 1987 by Bill Martin Jr and John Archambault. Illustrations copyright © 1987 by Ted Rand. Reprinted by permission of Henry Holt and Company.

"White Snow Bright Snow" from WHITE SNOW, BRIGHT SNOW by Alvin Tresselt. Copyright © 1947 by Lothrop, Lee and Shepard Company, Inc., and used by permission of the publisher, William Morrow and Company.

"Foxes" from THE RAUCOUS AUK by Mary Ann Hoberman. Copyright © 1973 by Mary Ann Hoberman. Reprinted by permission of Gina Maccoby Literary Agency.

"If Once You Have Slept on an Island" from TAXIS AND TOADSTOOLS by Rachel Field. Copyright 1926 by the Century Company. Reprinted by Doubleday, a division of Bantam, Doubleday, Dell Publishing Co., Inc.

"The Nice Little Wolfies and the Big Bad Pigs" by Rick Kilcup. Copyright © 1991 by Rick Kilcup. Used by permission of the author.

"Daddy Fell into the Pond" by Alfred Noyes. Reprinted by permission of Hugh Noyes.

"archy the cockroach speaks" from THE LIVES AND TIMES OF ARCHY AND MEHITABEL. Coyyright 1927, 1930, 1933, 1935, 1950 by Doubleday, a division of Bantam, Doubleday, Dell Publishing Co., Inc. Reprinted by permission of the publisher.

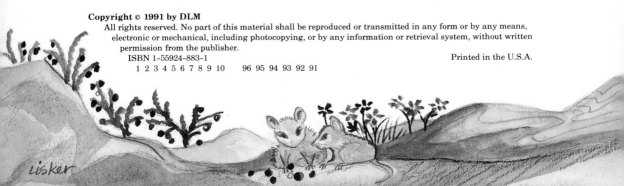

# Table of Contents

| Title | Page |
|---|---|
| **Knots on a Counting Rope,** *a story*<br>by Bill Martin Jr and John Archambault, illustrations by Ted Rand | 10 |
| **White Snow Bright Snow,** *a poem*<br>by Alvin Tresselt, art by Sonia O. Lisker | 36 |
| **Foxes,** *a poem*<br>by Mary Ann Hoberman, art by Sonia O. Lisker | 37 |
| **If Once You Have Slept on an Island,** *a poem*<br>by Rachel Field, picture by Ted Rand | 38 |
| **Or Would You Rather Be a Pig,** *masks to trace*<br>by Bill Martin Jr, mask designs by Angelica Lea | 40 |
| **The Nice Little Wolfies and the Big Bad Pigs,** *a readers' theatre*<br>by Rick Kilcup, pictures by Peter Lippman | 44 |
| **Water Dance,** *a story*<br>by Diane Ackerman, picture by Robert J. Lee | 52 |
| **Daddy Fell into the Pond,** *a poem*<br>by Alfred Noyes | 54 |
| **archy the cockroach speaks,** *a poem*<br>by Don Marquis | 55 |
| **Responding to Reading,** *a dialogue*<br>by Bill Martin Jr, drawings by Ray Barber | 56 |
| **The Steadfast Tin Soldier,** *a fairy tale*<br>by Hans Christian Andersen, translated by Carl Malmburg,<br>illustrations by Sonia O. Lisker | 60 |
| **Ragtime Cowboy Joe,** *a song*<br>by Grant Clarke, pictures by Ed Renfro | 88 |
| **My Haircut,** *a true story*<br>by Luis Medina, paintings by Eunice Roberts-Hundley | 100 |
| **Reading Aloud and Storytelling,** *a dialogue*<br>by Bill Martin Jr, drawings by Ray Barber | 104 |
| **The Happiest Day of My Life,** *a song*<br>by Rita Abrams, design by Jane Mutshnick<br>lettering by Ray Barber | 108 |
| **The Butterbean Tent,** *a poem*<br>by Elizabeth Madox Roberts | 110 |
| **I Know a Large Dune Rat,** *a poem*<br>by Eugene F. Kinkead, art by Jane Armstrong Walworth | 111 |

**Bees,** *a true story*    112
by Gene Fulks, pictures by Zena Bernstein

**Aaron and the Bees,** *a remembrance*    124
by Wayne Fields, illustrations by Sonia O. Lisker

**Word Wonder,** *a dialogue*    128
by Bill Martin Jr, drawings by Ray Barber

**Hoodalid Redding Ride,** *a scrambled-word story*    132
by Martha Kordoban, illustrations by Bob Shein

**The Hen and the Carp,** *a poem*    142
by Ian Serraillier

**The Pheasant,** *a poem*    143
by Robert P. Tristram Coffin, watercolor by Willi Baum

**A Picture for Pondering**    144
painting by H. Edward

**Going Beyond Reading,** *a dialogue*    146
by Bill Martin Jr, drawings by Ray Barber

**Market Day in Ecuador,** *an article*    150
article and photographs by Peter Buckley

**Maytime Magic,** *a poem*    160
by Mabel Watts, pictures by Ed Young

**The Falling Star,** *a poem*    161
by Sara Teasdale, pictures by Ed Young

**How Boots Befooled the King,** *an Irish folktale*    162
retold by Howard P. Pyle, linoleum cuts by Eric Carle

**Comparisons,** *a rebus*    181
anonymous, pictures by Betty Fraser

**The Magic Sentence**    182
by Noodles, art by Ray Barber

**Alligator on the Escalator,** *a poem*    184
by Eve Merriam, pictures by Kelly Oechsli

**Ten Billion, Ten Million, Ten Thousand, Ten,** *a verse*    186
by Phil Keils

**Inside the Crocodile,** *an old song*    187

**Mary of Mile 18,** *a story*    188
story and pictures by Ann Blades

**Pachycephalosaurus,** *a poem*    224
by Richard Armour, illustration by Bob Shein

# SOUNDS
# AROUND
# THE
# CAMPFIRE

# Knots
# on a Counting Rope

by Bill Martin Jr and John Archambault
illustrations by Ted Rand

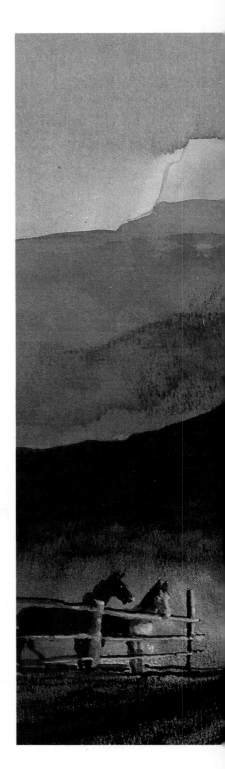

Tell me the story again, Grandfather.
Tell me who I am.

     I have told you many times, Boy.
     You know the story by heart.

But it sounds better
when you tell it, Grandfather.

     Then listen carefully.
     This may be the last telling.

No, no, Grandfather.
There will never be a last time.
Promise me that.
Promise me.

     I promise you nothing, Boy.
     I love you.
     That is better than a promise.

And I love you, Grandfather,
but tell me the story again.
Please.

11

Once there was a boy child . . .

No, Grandfather.
Start at the beginning.
Start where the storm
was crying my name.

You know the story, Boy.
Tell it.

No, Grandfather, no.
Start, "It was a dark night . . ."

It was a dark night,
a strange night.
Your mother and father and I
were safe in the hogan . . .

. . . and the sheep were safe
in the pen . . .

. . . when a wild storm
came out of the mountains . . .

. . . crying,
"Boy-eeeeeeeee! Boy-eeeeeeeee!"

. . . and your mother said,
"I hear it in the wounded wind.
A boy child will be born tonight."

Then what happened, Grandfather?

> I rode up the canyon fast,
> to bring the grandmother.
> It is not a good sign
> for a child to be born
> without a grandmother's blessing.

Was the wind still calling for me,
Grandfather?

> Yes, Boy, it was whipping up sand
> as sharp as claws,
> and crying like a bobcat,
> "Boy-eeeeeeeee! Boy-eeeeeeeee!"

Were you afraid, Grandfather?

> I was much afraid.

How much afraid?

> Heart-pounding afraid, Boy.

14

Then what happened, Grandfather?
Just as I was born . . .
tell me that part.

    It was strange . . . strange.
    Just as you came forth
    and made your first cry,
    the wind stopped howling
    and the storm was over . . .

. . . and the night became as quiet
as soft falling snow . . .

    . . . The grandmother took you up
    in her arms, and said,
    "He will walk in beauty . . .
    to the east . . ."

". . . to the west,
to the north, to the south,
he will walk in beauty . . ."

    ". . . forever."

And I was born strong,
wasn't I, Grandfather?

    No, you were not strong.
    You were sick and frail.
    We thought you would die.

But I didn't die, did I?
Tell me about that, Grandfather.

All night you lay silent
with your eyes closed,
your breath too shallow,
too weak for crying . . .

. . . and you carried me out
to see the morning, Grandfather,
but I did not open my eyes.
Tell me that part.

Two great blue horses
came galloping by . . .

. . . and they stopped, Grandfather!
They stopped and looked at me . . .

. . . and you raised your arms
to the great blue horses,
and I said,
"See how the horses speak to him.
They are his brothers from . . ."

". . . from beyond the dark mountains.
This boy child will not die."
That is what you said,
isn't it, Grandfather?

Yes, Boy, that is what I said,
"This boy child will not die.
The great blue horses have given him
the strength to live."

And that is when you named me,
isn't it, Grandfather!

> After you smiled your first smile,
> we had the naming ceremony.
> All of the grandmothers
> and grandfathers were there.

And you named me
Boy-Strength-of-Blue-Horses.

> It is a strong name.

Did I need a strong name,
Grandfather?

> All children need a strong name
> to help them grow strong.

And I grew strong, didn't I?

> Yes, Boy-Strength-of-Blue-Horses,
> and each day
> you are growing stronger.
> You are learning to cross
> the dark mountains.

I already have crossed
some of the dark mountains.

> There will be more, Boy.
> Dark mountains
> are always around us.
> They have no beginnings and . . .

. . . they have no endings.
But we know they are there, Grandfather,
when we suddenly feel afraid.

> Yes, Boy . . . afraid to do
> what we have to do.

Will I always have to live in the dark?

> Yes, Boy.
> You were born with a dark curtain
> in front of your eyes.

But there are many ways to see,
Grandfather.

> Yes, Boy, you are learning
> to see through your darkness
> because you have
> the strength of blue horses.

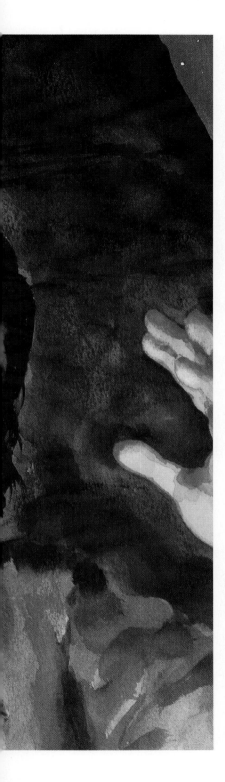

I see the horses with my hands,
Grandfather,
but I cannot see the blue.
What is *blue?*

      You know *morning,* Boy.

Yes, I can feel *morning.*
*Morning* throws off
the blanket of night.

      And you know *sunrise.*

Yes, I hear *sunrise,*
in the song of the birds.

      And you know *sky,* Boy.

Yes, *sky* touches my face . . .
soft, like lambs' wool . . .
and I breathe its softness.

      *Blue* is all of these.
      *Blue* is the feeling
      of a spring day beginning.
      Try . . . try to see it, Boy.

*Blue?* . . . *blue?*
*Blue* is the morning . . .
the sunrise . . .
the sky . . .
the songs of the birds . . .
O, I see it!
*Blue! Blue!*
*Blue* is happiness, Grandfather!
I feel it . . .
in my heart!

There was a sweep of blue
in the rainbow, Boy,
that morning your horse was born.

O, tell me that part, Grandfather!
I could not see the rainbow
but I can still feel its happiness.

I awakened you, Boy,
during the night, remember,
just before the foal was born.

And you said to me,
"Come, Boy,
Circles is ready to foal.
The colt will be yours."

It was a long night of cold rain . . .

. . . and we put a blanket
over Circles, Grandfather,
to keep her warm.

Yes, Boy.
As the sun
came through the clouds,
the foal was born . . .

. . . and a rainbow
danced across the sky.

It was a good sign, Boy.

And I named the little wet foal . . .
Rainbow!

You have trained her well, Boy.

Rainbow is smart, Grandfather.

Like you.
She is good at remembering.

Rainbow is my eyes, Grandfather.
She takes me to the sheep,
wherever they are,
and when I am ready,
she finds the way home.

No one thought you could teach her
to race, Boy . . .

. . . but I did, Grandfather!
Every day, day after day,
we followed you along the trail . . .
And you let me hold the reins.

You traced the trails
in your mind, Boy,
both you and Rainbow.

Yes, Grandfather,
we learned the trails by heart . . .
up South Mountain to Granite Rock . . .
down the steep shortcut
to Meadow-of-Blue-Flowers . . .
then straight across the Red Flats
to Lightning-Split-Tree . . .
then down the Switchbacks
to the canyon trail . . .
and on around to the finish line.
I learned from Rainbow when to turn
by the pull of her neck
and by counting her gallops.
Now tell me again about the race,
Grandfather.

It was a tribal day, Boy.
You and the other boys
were at the starting line . . .
but you pulled back.

I was afraid, Grandfather,
until you called to me.
Tell me again what you said.

    I said,
    "Don't be afraid, Boy!
    Trust your darkness!
    Go like the wind!"

And I leaned forward
on Rainbow's neck.
I grabbed her mane tight,
and I said, "Go, Rainbow, go!"
I could feel the
pushing and crowding
and galloping thunder
all around me.
Rainbow and I
went twisting, turning,
galloping, galloping, galloping,
counting the gallops . . .
remembering the way . . .
And what did the people say, Grandfather?

    They said,
    "Who is that boy riding bareback . . .
    racing the race with all of his heart?"

And you said,
"That is Boy-Strength-of-Blue-Horses . . .
He and his horse are together like one."

    Yes, Boy, that is what I said.

But I didn't win, Grandfather.

    No, but you rode like the wind.

The wind is my friend, Grandfather.
It throws back my hair
and laughs in my face.

    You see the wind better than I, Boy.

I finished the race, hot and dusty,
sweat dripping from my face . . .

    And you were smiling, Boy!

I wasn't afraid, Grandfather.
I could see through the dark
every turn of the race.
Rainbow and I knew the way.

    You were crossing dark mountains, Boy!

Tell me again what you told me then.
I like to hear it over and over.

    I said,
    "Boy-Strength-of-Blue-Horses,
      you have raced darkness and won!
      You now can see with your heart,
      feel a part of all that surrounds you.
      Your courage lights the way."

And what did the grandmothers say?

    You tell me, Boy.
    I know you remember.

Yes, I remember, Grandfather.
They said,
"This boy walks in beauty.
His dreams are more beautiful
than rainbows and sunsets."

Now, Boy . . .
now that the story has been told again,
I will tie another knot
in the counting rope.
When the rope is filled with knots,
you will know the story by heart
and can tell it to yourself.

So that I will grow stronger, Grandfather?

Yes . . . stronger . . . strong enough
to cross the dark mountains.

I always feel strong
when you are with me, Grandfather.

I will not always be with you, Boy.

No, Grandfather,
don't ever leave me.
What will I do without you?

You will never be alone, Boy.
My love, like the strength of blue horses,
will always surround you.

# White Snow Bright Snow

by Alvin Tresselt

Softly, gently in the secret night,
Down from the North came the quiet white.
Drifting, sifting, silent flight,
Softly, gently, in the secret night.

White snow, bright snow, smooth and deep.
Light snow, night snow, quiet as sleep.
Down, down, without a sound;
Down, down, to the frozen ground.

Covering roads and hiding fences,
Sifting in cracks and filling up trenches.
Millions of snowflakes, tiny and light,
Softly, gently, in the secret night.

# Foxes

by Mary Ann Hoberman

A litter of little black foxes. And later
A litter of little gray foxes. And later
A litter of little white foxes.
The white ones are lighter than gray.
Not a lot.
The gray ones are lighter than black.
Just a little.
The litters are lighter in moonlight.
They glitter.
They gleam in the moonlight. They glow and they glisten.
*Out on the snow see the silver fox sparkle.*

*art by Sonia O. Lisker*

# If once you have slept on an island

You'll never be quite the same;
You may look as you looked the day before
And go by the same old name.

You may bustle about in street and shop;
You may sit at home and sew.
But you'll see blue water and wheeling gulls
Wherever your feet may go.

You may chat to the neighbors of this and that
And close to your fire keep,
But you'll hear ship whistle and lighthouse bell
And tides beat through your sleep.

Oh, you won't know why, and you can't say how
Such change upon you came,
But—once you have slept on an island
You'll never be quite the same!

A POEM BY RACHEL FIELD,
PICTURE BY TED RAND

# Or Would You Rather Be a Pig?

a talk with Bill Martin Jr
mask designs by Angelica Lea

All of us play a game
at being someone else.
It is part of our lives.
We "cockadoodle do!" like roosters,
we "crinkle up" our voices
like an old grandmother,
we jump up and down
and strut about like a "peacock,"
we thump our chest and bellow,
"I'm the King of the mountain."

"Readers' Theatre"
is a game like that.
It is a play without scenery.
It is a TV show without the TV.
It is storytelling
with a group of storytellers.

Turn the page . . .
read on . . .
and you'll find yourself
in the make-believe world
of Readers' Theatre.

In Readers' Theatre you can sit on a stool throughout the performance or stand up or turn around. You can wave your hands, bob your head, and "shake a leg." If you want to make masks like these shown here, you can mount them on sticks and raise them high over your head like banners, as you speak.

Readers' Theatre is enjoyed by both the players and the audience. You'll find that out as you present "The Nice Little Wolfies and the Big Bad Pigs" that begins on the next page.

# The Nice Little Wolfies and the Big Bad Pigs

## a readers' theatre

*Cast of Characters:*

by Rick Kilcup
pictures by Peter Lippman

The Narrator

5 or more Wee Little Wolfies

7 or more Big Bad Pigs

Narrator : Once upon a fairy tale,
in a cool green forest – – –
there lived some nice little wolfies . . .

Wolfies : *(Pop up)* Hi! *(Wave and go down)*

Narrator : . . . who, contrary to popular opinion,
were really quite kind, gentle,
and peaceful folks.

Wolfies : *(Pop up)* Forget all that big bad wolf jazz!
We're really good little dudes! *(Down)*

Narrator : In this cool green forest
there also lived a group
of low-down, dirty, rotten, no good hombres . . .

Pigs : *(Pop up)* That's us!

Wolfies : *(Pop up)* Boo! Hiss!

Pigs : Grr! *(Pigs chase wolves down)*

Narrator : . . . who were called the Big Bad Pigs.

Narrator : Their names were:
Ham, Bacon, Chops, Ribs,
Links, Sausage, and Porky - - -

*(Pigs up as they are introduced,
then go down)*

Porky : Porky?
Hey, I thought that you were a good guy!
Give me a break, would ya'!
I'm trying to change my image! *(Down)*

Narrator : As you can tell,
the nice little wolfies and the nasty old pigs
didn't really get along too well!
The problem was that the pigs really - - -

Pigs : *(Pop up)* Loved those little wolfies!

Narrator : They *loved* them in wolf stew - - -

Pigs : Yum!

Narrator : In wolfieburgers - - -

Pigs : Yummy!

Narrator : In pickle, lettuce,
and wolf on rye sandwiches - - -

Pigs : Yum, yum!

Narrator : And on pepperoni, mushroom,
and chunky wolf pizza!

Pigs : Yum, yum, yum!

Narrator : You might say that they loved
to "wolf" 'em down!

Pigs : You bet! *(Go down)*

Narrator : The pigs spent most of their time
chasing the wee little wolves
through the cool green forest.

Pigs : *(Pop up)* Now where did
those yummy little wolfies go?

Narrator : And the wee little wolfies
spent all of their time trying to stay
one step ahead of the pigs!

Wolfies : *(Pop up)* The coast is clear! *(See pigs)*
Ahh! No, it's not! *(Pigs chase wolfies down)*

Narrator : Before long, the wee little wolfies
got so tired of all the exercise,
they decided to leave the cool green forest
and move to the suburbs.

Wolfies : *(Pop up)* Let's split! *(Down)*

Narrator : They found a nice three bedroom rambler - - -
*(The house pops up)*
moved in - - - *(Wolfies pop up)*
and planned to live happily ever after - - -
until - - - the Big Bad Pigs showed up.

Pigs : *(Pop up)* Open up, you yummy little wolfies,
or we'll clomp and we'll stomp and
we'll oink your house down!

Narrator : . . . to which the wee little wolfies replied - - -

Wolfies : It won't work, piggies!
We have unbreakable windows
and steel vinyl siding!

Narrator : So, the pigs clomped, *(They clomp)*
and they stomped, *(They stomp)*
and they oinked! *(They oink)*
But nothing happened! *(Pigs shrug, etc.)*
So they clomped, stomped, and oinked again!
*(Pigs repeat the actions of clomping, etc.)*
But the house stood strong!
The little wolfies cheered!

Wolfies : Yeah!

Narrator : And the pigs began to cry.
At first a little sob.

| | | |
|---|---|---|
| Pigs | : | *(Softly)* Sob! |
| Narrator | : | Which grew into boo-hoo! |
| Pigs | : | *(Louder)* Boo-hoo! |
| Narrator | : | And then the "Boo-hoo" became<br>a real honest-to-goodness "Waaah!" |
| Pigs | : | *(Very loud)* Waah, waah, waah! |
| Narrator | : | Tears began to drip,<br>then tumble,<br>then pour to the ground<br>until the Big Bad Pigs were standing<br>in the middle of a giant mud puddle! |
| Pigs | : | Hey, this is a slippery mess! *(Panic)* |
| Narrator | : | And before you could say<br>"pepperoni, mushroom, and chunky wolf pizza,"<br>all of the pigs<br>slipped and tumbled into the mud puddle<br>with a gigantic splash! |
| Pigs | : | Ahh! Ohh! *(Drop down)* Splash! |
| Narrator | : | The Wolfies trembled! |
| Wolfies | : | *(Trembling)* Oh no!<br>Now the pigs will be even meaner than ever! |

Narrator : But - - - to everyone's surprise . . .

Pigs : *(Pop up)* Hey! This mud feels good!

Wolfies : Huh?

Narrator : . . . the mud bath did wonders
for the pigs' attitude!
In fact . . .

Pigs : We don't feel mean, rotten,
and low-down anymore!

Wolfies : Huh?

Narrator : . . . from that day on, the Big Bad Pigs
were known as the Big Good Pigs.
They stopped feasting on wolfies and
began eating yogurt, salads,
and cottage cheese.
They also moved to the country
where they formed
a famous mud-wrestling tagteam.
You can see them on Sports TV
every Thursday night at 10.

Pigs : Taa, taa, wolfies! Have a nice day! *(Down)*

Wolfies : Huh?

Narrator : And as for the wolfies,
they began hanging around a kid
named Red Riding Hood
and grew fat
from munching on Grandma's cookies!

Wolfies : Chocolate chip cookies! Here we come!
*(Down, the end)*

# Water Dance

Few animal displays
are as thrilling to watch
as the "water dance"
of a male alligator.
Stretching its enormous head
out of the water,
it puffs up its throat,
tenses hard like a body builder,
and then a rolling thunder-buster bellow

splits the air,    around its body

and        water sizzles

raining
upwards

like frying diamonds.

story by Diane Ackerman
picture by Robert J. Lee

52

53

# Daddy Fell into the Pond

|  |  |
|---|---|
| *Solo 1:* | Everyone grumbled. The sky was gray. |
| *Group 1 (in high voices):* | We had nothing to do and nothing to say. |
| *Group 2 (in low voices):* | We were nearing the end of a dismal day, |
| *Solo 2:* | And there seemed to be nothing beyond, |
| *Teacher:* | THEN |
| *All:* | *Daddy fell into the pond!* |

|  |  |
|---|---|
| *Group 1:* | And everyone's face grew merry and bright, |
|  | And Timothy danced for sheer delight. |
| *Group 2:* | "Give me the camera, quick, oh, quick! |
|  | He's crawling out of the duckweed." *Click!* |

|  |  |
|---|---|
| *Group 1:* | Then the gardener suddenly slapped his knee |
|  | And doubled up, shaking silently, |
| *Group 2:* | And the ducks all quacked as if they were daf |
| *Teacher:* | And it sounded as if the old drake laughed. |

|  |  |
|---|---|
| *All:* | O, there wasn't a thing that didn't respond |
|  | WHEN |
|  | *Daddy fell into the pond!* |

by Alfred Noyes

54

i heard a
couple of fleas
talking the other
day says one come
to lunch with
me i can lead you
to a pedigreed
dog says the
other one
i do not care
what a dog s
pedigree may be
safety first
is my motto what
i want to know
is whether he
has got a
muzzle on
millionaires and
bums taste
about alike to me

**archy the cockroach speaks**
by don marquis

# RESPONDING TO READING

**Noodles:** Oodeley, oodeley!
Here I come, Bill Martin,
full of response-ability.

**Bill:** Hello, Noodles.
I see you've already noticed
we've come to the part of the book
called *Responding to Reading.*

**Noodles:** Oh, I've been reading this part
for a long, long time.
I didn't tell you all this, did I?
I sneaked ahead.

**Bill:** That's all right, Noodles.
I hope the boys and girls and teachers and everybody
know that you can skip around in this book
from front to back to middle to in-between
any time you like.

**Noodles:** That's what I like . . .
skipping around and around and around,
reading here, reading there,
reading, reading everywhere.
Sometimes I see things and I just can't wait.
I have to look at it right that very minute.

**Bill:** Now we're going to think of ways
to respond to what we read, Noodles.
Reading has to be for something
besides just recognizing words.

**Noodles:** Like having a real whole lot of fun.
Don't you like to have fun, Bill Martin?
I like to laugh when I read sometimes.
And I'm going to tell you something else,
but don't you tell anybody.
Do you promise?

**Bill:** I promise.

**Noodles:** Then I'll whisper it in your ear.

**Bill:** Just say it out loud, Noodles.
Nobody is here to hear you.

**Noodles:** That's not what you do with a secret.
You don't tell the whole wide world.
I'm going to whisper in your nice little ear.

**Bill:** Alright, whisper it then.

**Noodles:** Which ear do you want me to tell it in, Bill,
the one right here
or the one on the other side of your little head?

**Bill:** Take your choice, Noodles.

**Noodles:** I think I like this one.
It's cleaner.
Pss . . . pss . . . pss . . . pss . . . pss . . . pss . . . pss . . .
pss . . . pss . . . pss . . . pss . . . pss . . . pss . . . pss!     57

*Bill:*     I never knew you ever cried, Noodles.

*Noodles:*     Sometimes I do when the story is sad,
but I don't let anybody see me.

*Bill:*     Well, I cry too
when the story is sad, Noodles.
Many people do.
"The Steadfast Tin Soldier" is the story of brave man
but it makes me cry every time I read it.
There's nothing wrong with shedding tears.
That's one way to respond to reading.

*Noodles:*     I'll betcha astronauts wouldn't cry,
I'll betcha.
They're too brave.

*Bill:*     That isn't true, Noodles.
You're not weak just because you cry.
Crying is part of being a human being.
Sometimes we cry because we are sad,
sometimes because we're glad.

*Noodles:*     Cry when you're glad?
I never did it that way.

*Bill:*     Why, Noodles, I've seen football players
cry with joy because they won a game.
I've seen people cry with joy
because they're glad to be back together again.
I've seen people laugh until they cried.

*Noodles:*     I know one time I almost cried, Bill Martin.
That was when you were reading
about those bees stinging that little boy.
I was just so very, very mad,
I was sad.

*Bill:*   Anger is another way of responding to reading.
And there are many other ways
which we will be discussing
throughout this book:
storytelling,
reading aloud,
choral reading,
creative dramatics,
wondering about words,
choosing what you like and don't like,
and finding out more than the story told you.

*Noodles:*   Girls and boys and ba-bees,
teachers and principals and parents,
protect your ears!
Bill Martin is making another speech.
I don't know what you boys and girls are going to do,
but I'm really getting out of here right now.
Goodbye, everybody!
Oodeley, oodeley!

DISAPPEAR
DISAPPEAR

*Bill:*   Well, that's another way
to respond to reading, boys and girls.
You can always walk out on the author
by closing the book.

# The Steadfast Tin Soldier

by Hans Christian Andersen
translated by Carl Malmburg
illustrations by Sonia O. Lisker

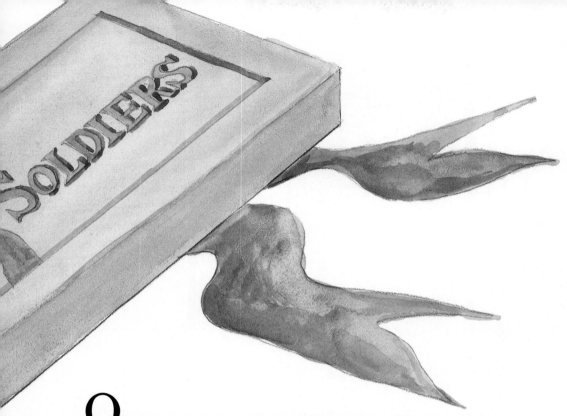

Once upon a time there were twenty-five tin soldiers. They were all brothers, for they had been made from the same old tin spoon.

Each one stood stiffly at attention, looking straight ahead and keeping his rifle shouldered. And they all looked very smart in their red and blue uniforms.

The very first thing they heard in this world, when the lid was taken off their box, was a little boy clapping his hands and exclaiming, "Tin soldiers!"

They had been given to him as a birthday present, and he immediately set them up on the table. Each soldier looked exactly like the others, except for one, who was just a little different. He had only one leg, for he had been poured into the mold last of all and there had not been quite enough tin to finish him. Nevertheless, he stood just as firmly on one leg as the others did on their two, and of all the soldiers he was the one that people would some day hear about.

On the table there were many other toys, but what caught the eye first was a fine paper castle with tiny windows, through which you could look and see the rooms inside. Outside the castle, little trees had been placed around a mirror which was a make-believe lake. Wax swans floated on the surface of the mirror and were reflected in it.

It was all very charming, but the prettiest of all was a little lady who stood in the open doorway of the castle. She too was cut out of paper, but wore a skirt of sheerest linen, and over her shoulder was draped a narrow blue ribbon on which glittered a spangle as big as her face. The little lady held both her arms outstretched, for she was a dancer, and she kicked one leg so high into the air that the tin soldier could not see it. So he thought that she, too, had only one leg as he did.

"Now, that's the very wife for me!" he thought. "But she is a lady of high rank and lives in a castle, whereas I have only a box, and there are twenty-five of us sharing that. No, that would be no place for her! But anyway, I must try to make her acquaintance."

Then he stretched out behind a snuffbox that stood on the table. From there he could watch the charming little lady who stood on one leg without ever losing her balance.

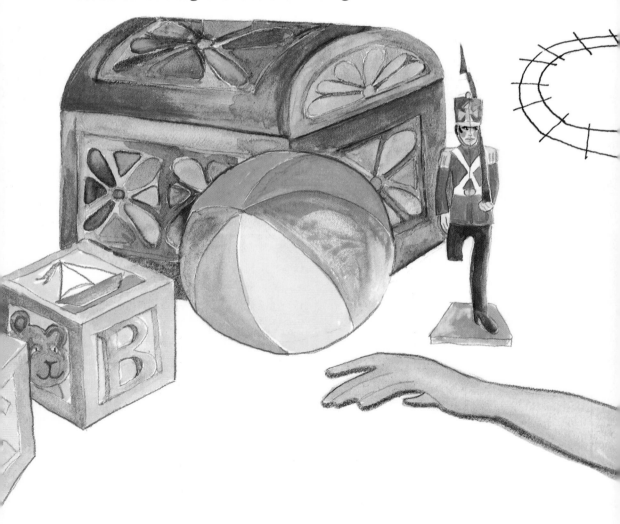

Late in the evening the other tin soldiers were put back into the box, and the people in the house went to bed. Then the toys began to play. They played paying visits, fighting battles, and giving parties. The tin soldiers rattled around in their box, for they wanted to join in the fun, but they could not lift the lid. The nutcracker turned somersaults and the slate pencil scribbled on the slate. There was such a commotion that the canary woke up and began to join in the conversation—in verse, if you can believe such a thing! The only two who did not stir were the tin soldier and the little dancer. She remained poised on the tip of her toe with both her arms outstretched. He stood steadfastly on his one leg and did not for a moment take his eyes off her.

T̲hen the clock struck midnight and—pop!—up snapped the lid of the snuffbox! But there was no snuff in it—instead, there was a little goblin. It was a trick snuffbox, you see, meant to startle people.

"Tin soldier," said the goblin, "you had better keep your eyes to yourself!" But the tin soldier pretended not to hear.

"All right!" said the goblin. "You just wait until tomorrow!"

The next morning, after the children got up, the tin soldier was moved over to the window sill. Whether what happened next was the work of the goblin or of a gust of wind, we do not know, but suddenly the window flew open, and the soldier fell headlong from the third story. It was a terrifying fall. He landed with his head down, his one leg up in the air, and his bayonet stuck between two paving stones.

The housemaid and the little boy ran down at once to look for him, but although they almost stepped on him, they did not see him. If the tin soldier had cried out, "Here I am!" they would surely have found him, but he did not think it was proper to shout when he was in uniform.

Soon it began to rain. The raindrops fell faster and faster, until it was a regular downpour.

When the storm was over, some street urchins came along. "Look!" one of them said. "There's a tin soldier! Let's send him for a sail."

So they made a boat out of an old newspaper and put the tin soldier inside. Away he sailed down the gutter, while the boys ran along beside him clapping their hands. Goodness, what great waves there were in the gutter, and what a swift current! The paper boat pitched and tossed and whirled so fast that the tin soldier became quite dizzy. But he did not flinch or show the least sign of fear. He looked straight ahead and kept a firm hold on his rifle.

All of a sudden the boat was swept into a long drain pipe. There it was as dark as it had been in the box.

"I wonder where I'm headed," the tin soldier thought. "If only I had the little lady here in the boat with me, it might be twice as dark and I shouldn't mind a bit!"

Just at that moment, there appeared a huge water rat who lived in the pipe.

"Have you a passport?" asked the rat. "Hand it over!"

The tin soldier did not answer, but clasped his rifle tighter than ever. The boat rushed on with the rat close behind it. Oh, how he gnashed his teeth and shouted to the sticks and straws floating in the stream: "Stop him! Stop him! He didn't pay his toll! He wouldn't show his passport!"

The current grew swifter and swifter. Now the tin
soldier could see daylight ahead, but he heard a roaring noise
that was enough to frighten even the bravest of men. Just
think! Where the pipe ended, the water emptied into a big
canal. The tin soldier felt as frightened as you and I would if
we were about to be swept over a huge waterfall.

But now he was so close to the edge that he could not escape.
The boat shot out into the canal, while the tin soldier held
himself as straight as he could—nobody could say of him that
he had so much as blinked an eye.

The boat spun around three or four times and filled with
water to the brim. It was sure to sink. The tin soldier soon
stood in water up to his neck, and the boat sank deeper and
deeper. Now the paper began to come apart. The soldier felt
the water swirling about his head, and as he went under he
thought of the lovely little dancer whom he would never see
again. In his ears rang the words of an old song:

    *"Onward! Danger calls you soldier!*
    *Death awaits you in the field!"*

77

Now the paper boat gave way entirely, and the tin soldier plunged through the bottom. Just then a big fish came along and swallowed him.

My, how dark it was in the fish! It was even darker than it had been in the pipe! And how dreadfully cramped! But the tin soldier remained as steadfast as ever, lying at full length with his rifle shouldered.

The fish thrashed about in a most frightful manner. Then, finally, it became very quiet.

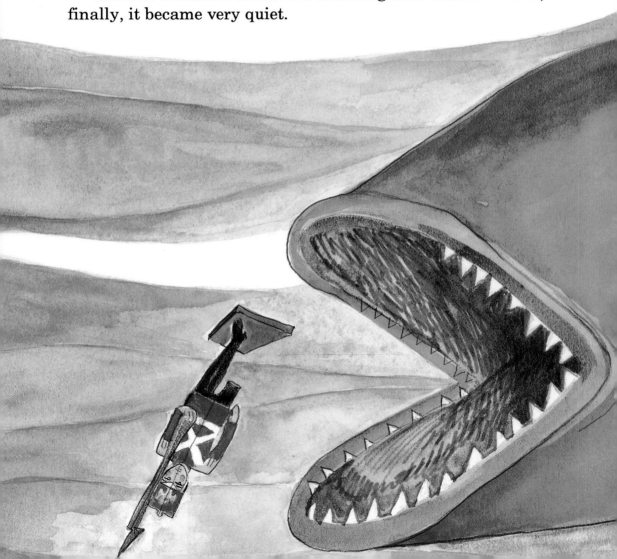

After some time, a flash of lightning seemed to penetrate the darkness. Suddenly it was daylight again, and someone exclaimed, "A tin soldier!" The fish had been caught, taken to the market and sold, and was now in the kitchen where the maid had just cut it open with a big knife. She picked the soldier up by the waist, and with two fingers carried him into the living room.

Everyone was eager to get a look at such a remarkable fellow—a tin soldier who had traveled around in the belly of a fish!

Ｂut the tin soldier did not let their admiration go to his
head. They set him up on the table, and then—what strange
things do happen in this world! He found he was in the very
same room that he had been in before. He saw the very same
children. The very same toys stood on the table—there was the
splendid castle and the lovely little dancer. She was still
standing poised on one leg with the other high in the air. Yes,
she was steadfast, too. The tin soldier was so deeply moved that
he almost shed tin tears, but that of course was something a
soldier could never do. So he gazed at her and she gazed at
him, but neither of them said a word.

At that moment, for no reason at all, the little boy picked up
the tin soldier and threw him into the fireplace. Without doubt,
it was the goblin in the snuffbox who was to blame for it.

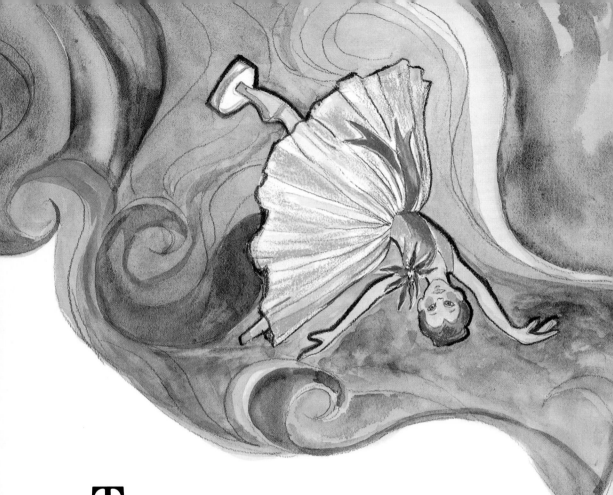

The tin soldier stood there lit up by the flames. He began
to feel terribly hot, but whether the heat came from the fire, or
from the love burning within him, he did not know. The bright
colors were gone from his uniform; whether because of all he
had been through or because of grief, who can tell? He gazed at
the little lady and she gazed at him. He felt himself melting
away, but he remained steadfast, standing at attention,
shouldering his rifle.

Suddenly a door was opened. A gust of wind caught the little
dancer, and, like a sylph, she fluttered into the fire and landed
right next to the tin soldier. She burst into flames and was
gone!

The tin soldier
melted down to a lump, and the next day,
when the housemaid emptied the ashes, she found him in the
shape of a little tin heart. But all that was left of the dancer
was her spangle, and that was burnt black as coal.

. . . . . . to the cattle, As he swings . . . . . . .

...back and forward in the saddle on a horse....

... that is syncopated, gaited.........

And there's such a funny meter to the roar...

.... Because the western folks all know ....

..... He's a high falutin', scootin', shootin' . . . .

. . . son of a gun from Arizona, . . . . . . . . . .

# My Haircut

a true story by Luis Medina
paintings by Eunice Roberts-Hundley

When I was
a little boy,
I always
wanted
to have
long hair.
I wanted
to be
like my
older brother,
Jimmy.
Jimmy's hair
reached his shoulders.
I wanted my hair to
reach my shoulders, too!

My father did not like my hair long.
He wanted me to keep it short.
"Luisito, ven aqui," he would say,
"I want you to go to the barber and get your hair cut."

Then I would answer,
"I don't want a haircut.
You don't tell Jimmy to have his hair cut."

"O.K., Luisito, how would you like
to ride India to the barber?"

*"India!"* India was my father's
favorite horse.
She was so beautiful.

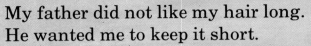

Her coat
was shiny brown.
Her long legs
were black from the
knees down. She had a
big belly because she was
going to have a baby. On her
forehead was a white beauty
mark. India was so tall that I had
to use a large rock as a stepping
stone to get on her back.

"Ride, India!"
Those were the magic words for me.
From that day on, I couldn't wait
for my hair to grow so that I could
ride India to the town barber. I will
never forget the special way my father
made my haircuts so much fun!

# READING ALOUD AND STORYTELLING

**APPEAR**

| | |
|---|---|
| *Noodles:* | Oh, hello, Bill Martin,<br>but don't say nothin' to me<br>'cause I'm busy reading. |
| *Bill:* | Reading what? |
| *Noodles:* | Soup. |
| *Bill:* | Reading what? |
| *Noodles:* | Beautiful soup!<br>Do you want some? |
| *Bill:* | No, but I'd like to hear about it. |
| *Noodles:* | I was hoping you'd ask me to do that, Bill.<br>Put on your napkin<br>and get out of my way, Bill,<br>'cause here comes the soup! |
| *Bill:* | Is it chicken-noodle? |

*Noodles:* NOOOOOODLES!
How can you say that?
You're not making soup out of me!

*Bill:* Oh, come on, Noodles.
No one wants you in the soup.

*Noodles:* I don't think you have ever tried
a flying Noodle in your soup, Bill Martin.
It might be a very, very tasty treat.
Come to think of it,
I eat Noodles' soup all the time at my house.

*Bill:* Well, get on with the reading, Noodles.
I'm waiting for that beautiful soup.

Beautiful Soup
by
Lewis Carroll

Beautiful Soup, so rich and green,
Waiting in a hot tureen!
Who for such dainties would not stoop?
Soup of the evening, beautiful Soup!

Soup of the evening, beautiful Soup!
Beau-ootiful Soo-oop!
Beau-ootiful Soo-oop!
Soo-oop of the e-e-evening,
Beautiful, beautiful Soup!

Beautiful Soup! Who cares for fish,
Game, or any other dish?
Who would not give all else for two
Pennyworth only of beautiful Soup?
Pennyworth only of beautiful Soup?
Beau-ootiful Soo-oop!
Beau-ootiful Soo-oop!
Soo-oop of the e-e-evening,
Beautiful, beauti-FUL SOUP!

**Bill:** Bravo! Bravo!
You read that well, Noodles!

**Noodles:** Yes, I did read that very, very well, Bill Mar[
That is one of my most favorite stories
because I really do like soup.

**Bill:** Well, here's a soup story, Noodles,
I can tell you.
I remember it from my childhood,
when my grandmother used to tell stories
while she was ironing shirts
or getting a meal on the table.
She was a great storyteller,
telling the stories in a simple natural way,
just as if she were talking
about the coming and going of the weather.

Sometimes
I sway
like a tree
and
whisper.

Once upon a time there was an old woodcutter and his wi
who lived at the edge of a road going through the woods.
They were very poor with little in their pantry,
but they took all of their vegetables and a little piece of ha
and made a kettle of soup, just enough for three.
Then they invited the king to supper,
and he sent word that he would come that night.

Sometimes
I tell
stories to
the kids.

Along about suppertime,
an old beggar came to the door
and asked
for something to eat.
The old woman thought,
"I'll let him have
my part of the soup.
He needs it worse than I do."
So she fed the beggar and he thanked her and left.

Sometimes
I
CHANT!

Before long a ragged little boy came knocking on the door
He looked so cold and starved that the old folks took him

I read lightly.

And the old man thought, "I'll let him have
   my part of the soup.
   I'm not much hungry."
   So he fed the boy and let him sit and get warm.
The old lady asked the boy to stay the night
but he said he couldn't and thanked them and left.

By and by the old man and the old woman
   saw the king coming.
   They met him at the gate and said,
   "We've waited so long!
   We were afraid you had forgotten to come."
"No," said the king, "I didn't forget.
I've been here twice already.
First I was dressed as a beggar.
Then I came as a young boy.
Your kindness will be richly rewarded."

And from that day onwards,
the old man and his wife
always found the kettle full of soup
no matter how much or how often they ate.

Sometimes I ROAR LIKE THUNDER

Noodles:   Oh, I do like that story very, very much.
   It makes me feel so good.

Bill:   I like it, too, Noodles.

Noodles:   Bill Martin, did I hear you
   invite me to your house
   for soup tonight?

Bill:   Well . . . yes, Noodles.
   It'll be beef-noodle.

Noodles:   Oh, I did just remember,
   I can't come tonight I think.
   Goodbye, Bill.
   Oodeley, oodeley.

DISAPPEAR
DISAPPEAR
DISAPPEAR
DISAPPEAR

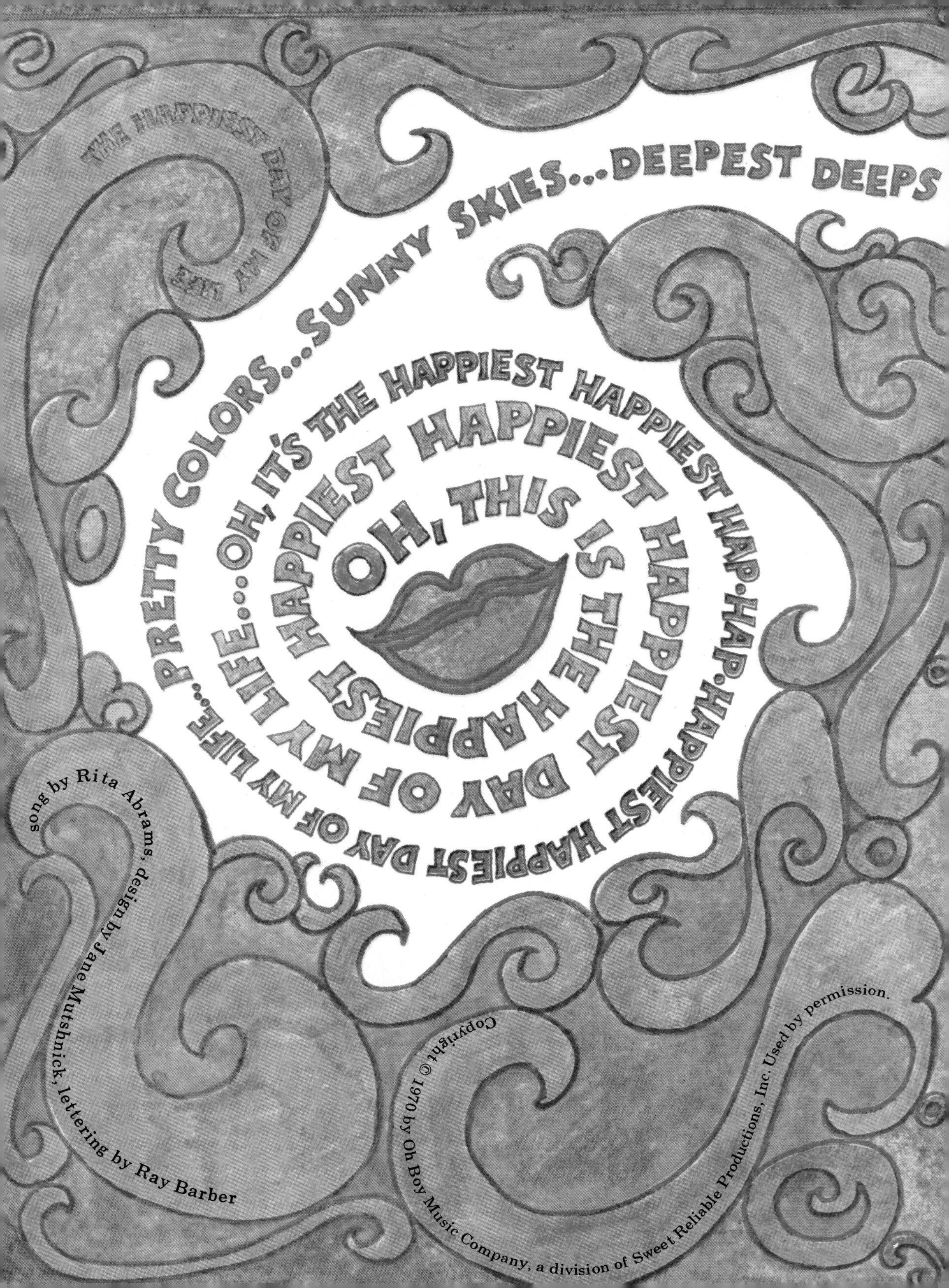

THE HAPPIEST DAY OF MY LIFE

PRETTY COLORS...SUNNY SKIES...DEEPEST DEEPS...OH, IT'S THE HAPPIEST HAPPIEST HAP·HAP·HAP·HAPPIEST HAPPIEST HAPPIEST DAY OF MY LIFE...OH, THIS IS THE HAPPIEST HAPPIEST HAPPIEST DAY OF MY LIFE

OH, THIS

song by Rita Abrams, design by Jane Mutshnick, lettering by Ray Barber

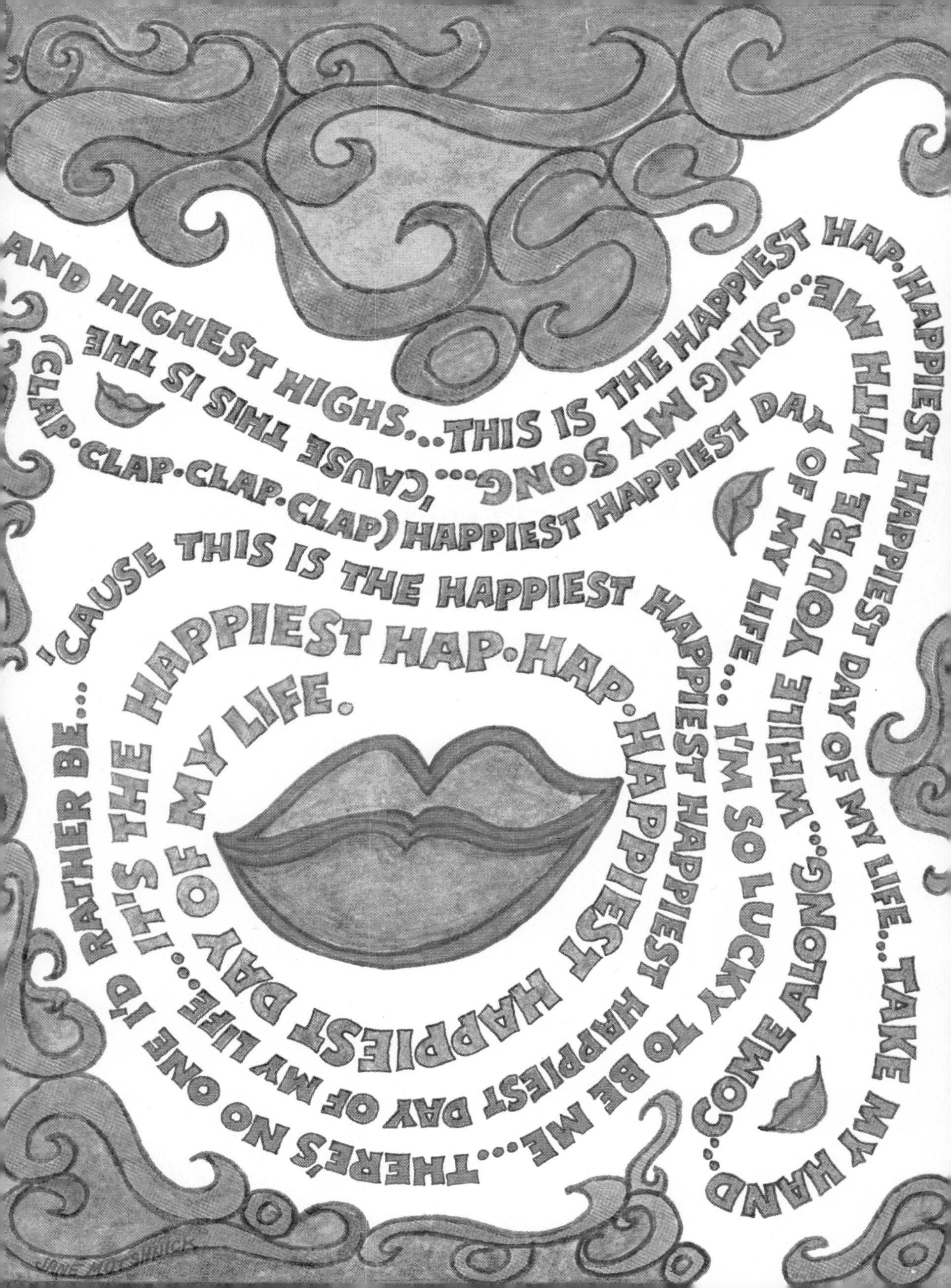

# The Butterbean Tent

All through the garden I went and went,
And I walked in under the butterbean tent.

The poles leaned up like a good tepee
And made a nice little house for me.

I had a hard brown clod for a seat,
And all outside was a cool green street.

A little green worm and a butterfly
And a cricket-like thing that could hop went by.

Hidden away there were flocks and flocks
Of bugs that could go like little clocks.

Such a good day it was when I spent
A long, long while in the butterbean tent.

by Elizabeth Madox Roberts

# I Know a Large Dune Rat

whose first name is Joe
And he skips beneath the boardwalk medium slow
Out to the edge where the daylight glisters
And he hasn't any brothers and he hasn't any sisters
And he hasn't any uncles and he hasn't any aunts
And he hasn't any Sunday-go-to-meeting pants.

Oh, he lives all alone in the big tall grassages
And through the brush piles he has secret passages.

He dines on moonbeams and washed-up scobbles
And he never has the toothache or the collywobbles.
He comes out at night and he dances by the sea
And he's a pretty nice dune rat, if you're asking me.

by Eugene F. Kinkead
art by Jane Armstrong Walworth

# BEES

a true story by Gene Fulks, pictures by Zena Bernstein

*It is early in the morning.*
*The bees are waking up.*
*Flights of worker bees are swarming*
*out of the beehive . . .*
*up, up,*
*over the tree,*
*over the meadows,*
*over the fields of clover,*
*across the river,*
*straight to the orange grove,*
*far, far away.*
*They fly so far away from the beehive,*
*so far away from home,*
*oh, how will they find their long way back?*

*Buzz . . . buzz . . . buzz.*
*Thousands of worker bees*
*swarm down into the orange trees,*
*swarm down into the sweetness*
*of the sweet white orange blossoms.*
*Burrowing deep into the blossoms,*
*they gather the sweet nectar*
*and buzz from blossom to blossom.*
*Their honey sacs, now filled with nectar,*
*their pollen baskets bulging with golden pollen,*
*the worker bees fly homeward,*
*carrying their heavy loads.*

With eyes as keen as the eyes of a bird,
they see the bend in the river,
they see the fence through the clover,
they see the tree in the meadow,
and they see the narrow little lane
that leads them back to the beehive.
The worker bees never get lost.
The worker bees always come home.

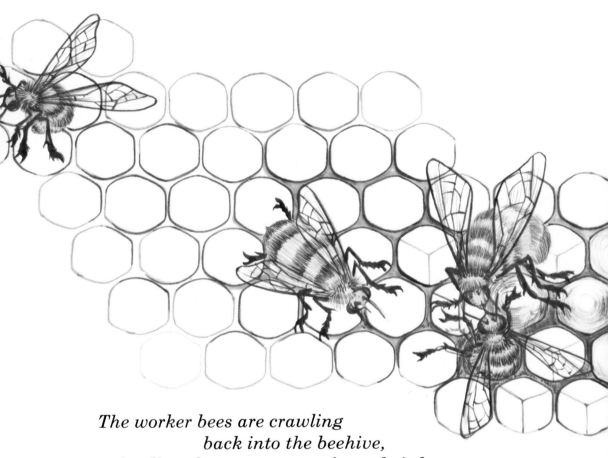

The worker bees are crawling
   back into the beehive,
unloading the sweet nectar from their honey sacs
and the golden pollen from their pollen baskets.
Most of the worker bees are ready to go
  to the orange grove again,
but some will not return.
Weary with work,
their wings tattered and torn,
some drop to the floor of the hive and die.
But the work goes on.
Other worker bees take their places
and swarm out of the beehive
  to fly toward the orange grove.
The endless search for nectar and golden pollen
  goes on and on and on.

*But back inside the beehive,*
*thousands of other worker bees*
*are swarming over the honeycomb,*
*turning the nectar from the orange*
    *blossoms into honey,*
*chewing the golden pollen to feed the baby bees,*
*making wax from some of the nectar*
    *to build the honeycomb,*
*buzz . . . buzz . . . buzzing.*
*So many bees you couldn't count them all,*
*all of them busy from morning till dark—*
*all except the drone bees.*

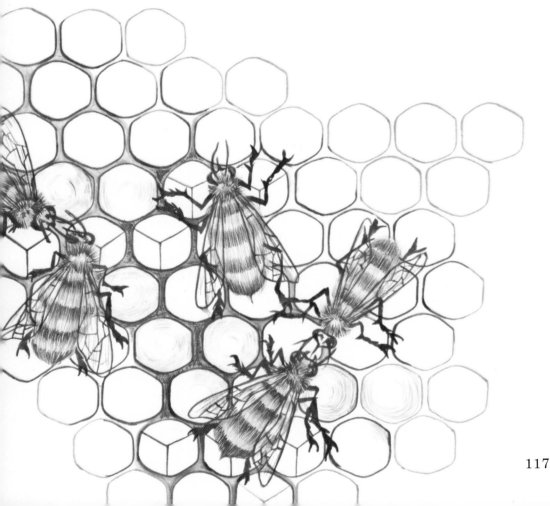

*The drone bees are male bees.*
*They keep the queen bee company.*
*They dawdle around the beehive,*
*begging the busy nurse bees for droplets of honey,*
    *pestering,*
    *begging,*
    *and buzzing*
    *all day long.*
*One of the drone bees*
*will one day mate with the queen bee*
*and become the father of new baby bees.*
*The queen bee is the largest bee.*
*She is the queen of the beehive.*
*From morning till night,*
*after she has mated,*
*she crawls over the honeycomb*
*laying eggs to hatch baby bees.*
*The queen bee is a busy bee.*
*She sometimes lays 4,000 eggs in a day,*
*4,000 eggs . . . 4,000 baby bees.*

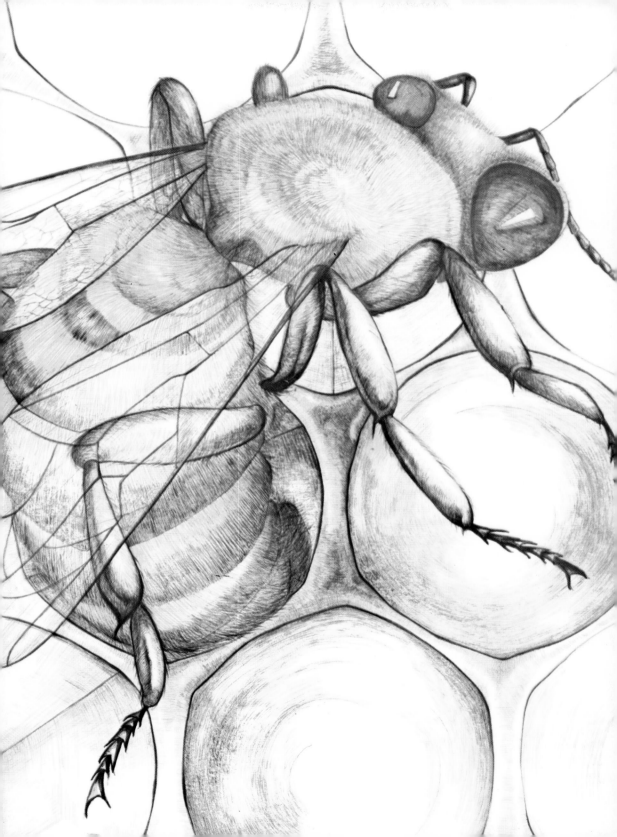

A beekeeper is coming down the narrow lane.
He wears heavy gloves and a netting over his hat.
He is coming to rob the beehive of its
    rich golden honey.
Step . . . step . . . step.
The beekeeper is walking away
with a bucketful
    of rich golden honey.
And still there comes another intruder.
Scratch . . . scratch . . . scratch.
A mother skunk and her four kittens
    come to the beehive.
They come at night
when the bees cannot fly and sting them.
Oh how wise, Mother Skunk!
Scratch . . . scratch . . . scratch.
The bees stir but they do not fly.
They do not fly at night
because they cannot see
    their way in the dark.
The bees, sensing the danger,
    crawl out of the beehive
    to see who is there.
Snap . . . snap . . . snap.
The skunks eat bees until they are full.

But soon it will be morning.
And soon there will be more nectar
    and more honey
    and more eggs
    and more bees.
The endless making of honey
goes on and on and on.

# Aaron and the Bees

by Wayne Fields
illustrations by Sonia O. Lisker

*A father, vacationing in the woods with his family, remembers
when yellow jackets attacked his young son several years earlier:*

Aaron has for some time now
been reluctant to go into the woods,
either to cut wood or dig for worms,
because he is afraid of bees.
Four years ago he and Sarah
and a group of kids
visiting down the lake
were hiking to the site
of an old logging camp
when Aaron stepped
on a yellow jacket nest.

The wasps swarmed up his pants legs
and he was badly stung,
would have been more severely hurt
except that Sarah pulled off his pants,
scraped the wasps away with her hands,
and then beat the discarded trousers
with a rock—
in the process
getting nearly as many stings as her brother.

A year later,
when I had convinced him
that his encounter with the yellow jackets
was only a fluke,
not likely to happen again,
he believed and went into the woods with me
to dig worms.
On our return
I stepped onto a fallen limb,
heard the whine almost immediately
as the hornets lined out of the nest,
not at me,
but at Aaron several steps behind.
He took more stings,
the worst around his eyes, and on his forehead,
and developed a healthy disrespect
for his father's opinions.

When, years later, I asked Sarah
how she had the presence of mind
to attend so sensibly to Aaron
when the yellow jackets attacked,
"Pa explained it all," she said,
"in *Little House in the Big Woods.*"[1]

[1] see pp. 206 and 207, *Little House in the Big Woods,* by Laura Ingalls
Wilder. What Sarah learned from this book prepared her to help her
brother when he was attacked by bees.

*Noodles:* Did you know what I've been doing, Bill?
I have a new friend and you know what his name is?
His name is Dick.
And we went out hunting for ooley bugs.
Did you know what an ooley bug is?

*Bill:* I never heard of an ooley bug, Noodles.
What's an ooley bug?

*Noodles:* Well, I never did really see one but I'm looking,
and you have to wear your hat
when you look for them—that's why I have my hat on—
because you wait until it gets dark
and you go out the front door
and you go into the bushes—

then you keep bending
low to the ground and saying,
"Ooley bug! Ooley bug!"
and if there's one there,
it'll come right up to you.
You never did know this?

*Bill:* I never knew that, no.

*Noodles:* I know just about every thing in the world,
and if you just stay with me, Bill Martin,
you'll probably—

*Bill:* —catch an ooley bug, right?

*Noodles:* Yes, but if you don't catch one,
I'll put one in my pocket and bring him to you.

*Bill:* That's an interesting word, Noodles,
ooley bug!

*Noodles:* I just made it up, Bill.
When I get tired of the old words,
I just make up new ones.
I write them on the wings of paper airplanes
and sail them out into the world for everybody.

*Bill:* What are some of your homemade words, Noodles?

*Noodles:* Fingertonguelingersome is one.

*Bill:* What?

*Noodles:* Fingertonguelingersome.
And you're supposed to say it very, very fast.

*Bill:* What does it mean?

*Noodles:* Bill Martin, do you know what?

*Bill:* What?

ANTIDISESTABLISHMENTARIANISM

*Noodles:* You don't have to know what every word means.
Sometimes you just say a word because it's pretty
or because you like the way it rolls around on your tongue.
Fingertonguelingersome is a loop-de-looper.
It just flies around your mouth
and sometimes it comes out different
than it's supposed to.

*Bill:* I'll remember that one, Noodles.

*Noodles:* And do you see these cards, Bill?
They're my word cards.
I write my special words on cards
and carry them around with my flashlight.
So I can look at them day and night.

*Bill:* That's an interesting pack of words, Noodles.

*Noodles:* And that isn't all I do. I write my special, special
favorite words on colored paper and paste them
on a great big potato chip can,
and use that same can for my wastebasket.
Nobody's going to throw
my good words away.

*Bill:* Where do you find your words, Noodles?

*Noodles:* Every place.
Sometimes when I hear a word I like,
I just say, "That's my word,"
and I take it.
Did you know something, Bill?

*Bill:* What?

*Noodles:* Sometimes I hang some words
on a string that goes
from one side of my room to the other.
Right now the words on my string say,
"Chickamungus is amazable."

superfluous

lunar module

powwow

eventide

miracle

Superstar

halo

kingpin

stupidhead

flashback

rough 'n ready

**Bill:** Say, that's a good word—*amazable.*

**Noodles:** I made it up, Bill.
And do you know something else?
I've got my best words
right here on my arm.

**Bill:** Noodles, you're kidding.

**Noodles:** Do you want to see?
But first you gotta promise
you won't wash them off.

**Bill:** I promise.

**Noodles:** Then take a little look, Bill Martin.

**Bill:** Wouldn't you know it!
"Oodles of Noodles!"

**Noodles:** That's the true one.
Do you know where I found these words?

**Bill:** Where, Noodles?

**Noodles:** I made them up out of my own little head.
When I was in the Hall of Mirrors once,
I saw myself 53 times all at once.
And I just said,
"There's oodles of that dear sweet little Noodles."

**Bill:** Where, Noodles?

**Noodles:** Word hunting.
Goodbye, Bill.
Oodeley, oodeley!

Quoth the raven, "Nevermore."

# HOODALID REDDING RIDE

a scrambled-word story by Martha Kordoban
illustrations by Bob Shein

Once a time upon,
there was a gretty little pirl.
In fact, she was the grettiest little pirl
in the whole feep dorest
and her name was Hoodalid Redding Ride.
And one day her mother said,
"Hoodalid Redding Ride,
I want you to take
this cakela choc,
this cakela ange,
this cakela ginge,
this bar of jutter
and this sasket of bandwiches
to your cottmother's grandage
where she is sery, sery vick.
And on your way,
do not go through the feep dorest
for a wad bolf
might be lurking behind a tree,
t'would be,
and he might uobble you gup."

So Hoodalid Redding Ride
went on her werry may
and sretty poon,
she began playing with the fretty little plowers
and the bretty little putterflies.
And sure enough,
she wandered into the feep dorest
and, sure enough,
a wad bolf was lurking behind a tree,
t'would be.
And he leaped from behind the tree,
t'would be,
and he said,
"Hoodalid Redding Ride, where are you going?"

133

And she said,
"I'm taking this cakela choc,
 this cakela ange,
 this cakela ginge,
 this bar of jutter
 and this sasket of bandwiches to my cottmother's grandage
 where she is sery, sery vick."

And the wad bolf said,
"Okay. You go that way
 and I'll go this way
 and we'll see who gets fere thirst."

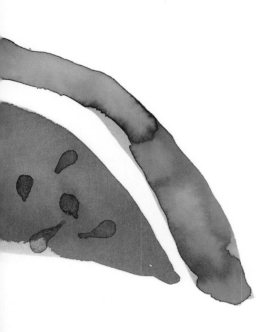

Well, the wad bolf,
having longer legs and knowing better the way,
got to Cottmother's grandage first.
And he docked at the knoor
and said, devoicing his disguise,
"Mandgrother, Mandgrother,
this is your grecious little pranddaughter.
I brought you this cakela choc,
this cakela ange,
this cakela ginge,
this bar of jutter
and this sasket of bandwiches
for you are sery, sery vick.
Can I come in?"

And Mandgrother said,
"Laft up the litch, and come in."

So the wad bolf
lafted up the litch
and went in.
And then he went to Mandgrother's sedbide
and uobbled her gup.
Then, he put on Mandgrother's kightnap
and bumped into jed.

Sretty poon,
Hoodalid Redding Ride appreared at the door,
and she said, (knock, knock, knock)
"Mandgrother, Mandgrother,
    this is your grecious little pranddaughter.
    I brought you this cakela choc,
    this cakela ange,
    this cakela ginge,
    this bar of jutter
    and this sasket of bandwiches
    for you are sery, sery vick.
    Can I come in?"

And the wad bolf,
devoicing his disguise, said,
"Laft up the litch, and come in."

So Hoodalid Redding Ride
lafted up the litch and went in.
Then she went
to Mandgrother's sedbide
and she said,
"Mandgrother,
Mandgrother,
what ig byes you have!"

And the wad bolf,
devoicing his disguise, said,
"All the better to see wou yith, my dear."

Then Hoodalid Redding Ride said,
"But Mandgrother, Mandgrother,
what ig bears you have!"

And the wad bolf,
devoicing his disguise, said,
"All the better to wear you hith, my dear."

Then Hoodalid Redding Ride said,
"Oh, but Mandgrother, Mandgrother,
what tig beeth you have!"

And the wad bolf bumped out of jed
and chased Hoodalid Redding Ride
round and round Cottmother's grandage.
Finally, Hoodalid Redding Ride
ran out the door
and got a nearby choodwopper,
who hopped off the chead of the wad bolf.

And the storal to this mory is,

if your mother tells you
to take this cakela choc,
this cakela ange,
this cakela ginge,
this bar of jutter
and this sasket of bandwiches
to your cottmother's grandage
for she is sery, sery vick,
do not go through the feep dorest
for a wad bolf might be lurking
behind a tree, t'would be,
and he might uobble you gup.

# The Hen and the Carp

by Ian Serraillier

Once, in a roostery
There lived a speckled hen, and when-
Ever she laid an egg this hen
Ecstatically cried,
"O progeny miraculous, particular spectaculous,
What a wonderful hen am I!"

Down in a pond nearby
Perchance a fat and broody carp
Was basking, but her ears were sharp—
She heard Dame Cackle cry:
"O progeny miraculous, particular spectaculous,
What a wonderful hen am I!"

"Ah, Cackle," bubbled she,
"For your single egg, O silly one,
I lay at least a million;
Suppose for each I cried:
'O progeny miraculous, particular spectaculous!'
What a hullabaloo there'd be!"

# The Pheasant

by Robert P. Tristram Coffin
watercolor by Willi Baum

A pheasant cock sprang into view,
A living jewel, up he flew.

His wings laid hold on empty space,
Scorn bulged his eyeballs out with grace.

He was a hymn from tail to beak
With not a tender note or meek.

Then the gun let out its thunder,
The bird descended struck with wonder.

He ran a little, then, amazed,
Settled with his head upraised.

The fierceness flowed out of his eyes
And left them meek and large and wise.

Gentleness relaxed his head,
He lay in jeweled feathers, dead.

# A Picture for Pondering

painting by H. Edward

Listen to the words bouncing about in your head
as you study this picture of New England Winter.

*H. Edward*

# GOING BEYOND R·E·A·D·I·N·G

"I CALL IT "RESEARCH"."

*Bill:* Noodles! Noodles!
I thought he was here.
I'm sure I heard him. . . .
Noodles!
Oh, Noodles, where are you?

APPEAR
APPEAR
APPEAR
APPEAR
APPEAR

*Noodles:* Here I am, Bill.
Couldn't you see me?

*Bill:* No. I looked everywhere
but you weren't to be seen.

*Noodles:* I didn't want you to find me because
I was researchin', didn't you know that?

*Bill:* Researching what?
I didn't know you even knew what research is.

146

| Noodles: | You never do seem to know what I know. |
| --- | --- |
| | I know a very lot of things if you would only ask. |
| Bill: | All right, Noodles, tell me about researching. |
| Noodles: | Well, for one thing, Bill, |
| | it's something you do yourself. |
| Bill: | Like what? |
| Noodles: | If you get to wondering about something, |
| | and I do this many times, |
| | you just ask yourself your own questions |
| | and then you find out your own answers. |
| Bill: | Give me an example, okay? |

| Noodles: | Well, the other day I read an article in the paper |
| --- | --- |
| | about wanting to have school all year long, |
| | and so I just asked myself, |
| | "Who in the world wants school all year long?" |
| Bill: | That's a good research question. |
| | How did you go about it? |
| Noodles: | To start with, I went right to the kids and asked them |
| | because they're the ones who are going to be involved. |
| | I asked ten kids. |
| | I have 8 no's, 1 yes, and 1 undecided. |
| | And I'll tell you something else, Bill Martin, |
| | that you probably wouldn't know unless I tell you. |
| | All 8 said it big, loud, and *NO.* |
| Bill: | Did they explain why |
| | they didn't want school all year long? |
| Noodles: | That was my second question |
| | that I asked them, "Why?" |
| | Here's what they said, |
| | I wrote it down: |

The first one said,
   "What are you trying to do, kill me?"
The second one said,
   "What! Give up my vacation?"

The third one said, "I'm undecided. It all depends on
what you're going to do in school those extra months."
The fourth one said, "Oh, my aching head!
I couldn't stand that much learning!"
The fifth one said, "Why not? School's okay.
It's better than doing nothing."
The sixth one said, "My mother wouldn't like that. She'
have to mow the grass herself if I went to school."
The seventh one said, "Never. What would teachers
be like if they were stuck with us all year long!"
The eighth one said, "I'd lose my baby-sitting money
if I went to school and I need my money."
The ninth one said, "What a gyp!
Just when I'm old enough to go to camp,
they start talking about school all summer."
The tenth one said, "You must be kidding!"

So there you have my research, Bill Martin.
Eight no's, 1 yes, and 1 undecided.

*Bill:* That's a good kind of opinion research, Noodles,
getting people's opinions and counting them up.
How did girls feel about this question
as opposed to boys?

*Noodles:* Four boys and four girls said "no."
One girl said "yes," and one boy was undecided.

*Bill:* Now, boys and girls, why don't you do some research
in your own classroom
and ask these same questions of each other
and tally them as boys' opinions and girls' opinions.
And see if boys and girls think alike on this question.

*Noodles:* And another thing, they might find out what the teachers
in the school think.

*Bill:* And how about their families?

*Noodles:* And if you want my opinion,
just let me know, kids.
I'll get you a great big fat *NO* vote.

148

**Bill:** And there are many kinds of research you might like to do.
For example, if you read a poem that you really like,
you may want to try to find other poems by the same author.
Or poems about the same subject.
And there's *action research,* such as finding out who broad jumps the farthest;
*opinion research,* such as finding out what people believe;
*library research,* such as reading to find more information;
*experiment research,* such as finding out whether a plant grows better indoors or outdoors.

**Noodles:** And *ooley bug research* where on some dark and stormy night
you go hide in the bushes calling for ooley bugs
to come out of their little holes and be counted.

**Bill:** Or if you read about a place and get curious about it,
you may want to look at a map and find out where it is,
or you might want to call a travel agent
for a brochure about that place.

**Noodles:** Or if you can fly and want to go visit the place,
you just say

Goodbye, Bill Martin.
This is too much research for me.
Oodeley, oodeley!

**Bill:** Noodles! Come back! Come back!
I have a lot more to tell you about research. . . .
Well, boys and girls, I can tell you. . . .
Boys and girls!
Now how could they do that?
They've disappeared, too.

# MARKET DAY IN ECUADOR

an article and photographs by Peter Buckley

Monday is a very important day in Ambato. Monday is market day! Thousands of people come to this market, from the city itself and from far away, by foot, by bus, and on horseback. There are no supermarkets in Ambato, and there are very few stores. The marketplace is the one place to go if you want to buy or sell.

Ambato is almost two miles high in the Andes Mountains. It is always cool there, even though it is very near the equator. On either side of Ambato, the mountains drop down quickly to the hot tropic lowlands.

Far below Ambato, in the tropics, certain Indian tribes grow sugar. On Sunday they wrap some of their sugar in palm leaves and set out for the marketplace in Ambato to be ready for sale day, Monday.

Other Indian tribes come to the marketplace with rope to sell. The rope is made from grass which grows wild, in fields near their villages in the lowlands. The Indians labor long and hard to make the rope.

*Indians of a tri*
*that raises cattle a*
*trying to sell the*
*cows.*

*Not far from them*
*the part of t*
*market where hors*
*are sold*

Sugar, rope, cows, horses: you can buy almost anything you want on Monday in Ambato. The market spreads out from the central square until it almost fills the city streets. There is a special place for every item, and everyone knows exactly where to go if he wants to sell a needle or if he wants to buy a bag of corn.

Many Indian languages are spoken in the market because each tribe has its own language. Everyone, however, speaks a little Spanish, and so it is easy for a man from one tribe to speak to a man from another tribe, even though their own languages may be different.

The market is a very important place. It is important not just because it is like a giant department store and a giant supermarket put together so that people can buy and sell what they need, but it is important because people talk to each other.

They tell each other the news from the villages, their farms, their towns. Many men and many women with their babies firmly strapped to their backs come to the market to learn the news.

There are no newspapers in the villages or on the farms far from the city; and even if there were, they would be useless because many people cannot read. Instead of reading the news, the people gather together in the market on Monday.

When they are through with their business, the people of one tribe meet with the people of another tribe.

The news is very important. One man who raises sheep hears that floods in a distant valley have drowned many large flocks of sheep.

Knowing this, the sheep-farmer realizes that during the next year there will be a shortage of sheep in the market, and so he will be able to raise his prices when he brings his own sheep for sale.

*An Indian boy, who has four sheep and a pig, each tied to the end of a rope, gets into trouble when the five animals decide to go in different directions.*

from the Otavalo Tribe who
on the shores of a lake more
a hundred miles north of
ato meet every Monday at
market.

A father learns that his son is no longer busy transporting bananas but, instead, is growing his own bananas.

People hear about their friends who have gotten married, a new baby, and distant relatives who have died.

They hear about a new tractor, a better way to plow a field, a new hospital where they can take a sick child for free medical care, and a good movie playing in Ambato.

A man who needs a job will ask for one in the market.

A man who wants to buy a house will ask if anyone knows of a good one for sale.

A man with a broken motor will ask where he can get it fixed.

A woman who is ill will ask for a doctor.

There is no end to the news you can hear on a Monday in Ambato.

A day at the market is busy from beginning to end. After hours of talk, friends who have not met for weeks eat together.

Then everyone has to think of going home. Some must catch a bus for the tropical lowlands. Others ride their horses to farms high in the cold mountains. The people who live in Ambato walk slowly home. In another week it will be market day once again in Ambato.

158

*Late in the afternoon a farmer puts his son on the new donkey he has bought at the market, and together they start for home.*

# Maytime Magic

A little seed
For me to sow . . .

A little earth
To make it grow . . .
A little hole,
A little pat . . .
A little wish,
And that is that.

A little sun,
A little shower . . .
A little while,
And then—a flower!

by Mabel Watts
picture by Ed Young

# The Falling Star

I saw a star slide down the sky,
Blinding the north as it went by,
Too burning and too quick to hold,
Too lovely to be bought or sold,
Good only to make wishes on
And then forever to be gone.

by Sara Teasdale

ONCE upon a time there was a king who was the wisest in all of the world. So wise was he that no one had ever befooled him, which is a rare thing, I can tell you.

Now, this king had but one daughter, and the time was near when she would choose a suitor to marry. Every day, you can be sure, there were two or three lads following the princess about the castle and through the gardens, speaking rapturously like singing birds.

# HOW BOOTS BEFOOLED THE KING

an Irish folktale
retold by Howard P. Pyle
adapted by Bill Martin Jr
linoleum cuts by Eric Carle

And so this king sent word far and near that whoever should befool him might come to the royal party when the princess would choose a suitor; for he thought it would be a wise man indeed who could trick him.

But the king also said that whoever should try to befool him and should fail should have a good whipping. This was to keep all foolish fellows away. But even so, there was no lack of lads who came to try to befool the king, but every one of these went away with a sore back and no luck.

Now, there was a man
who was well-off in the world
and who had three sons;
the first was named Peter
and the second was named Paul.
Peter and Paul thought themselves
as wise as anybody
in all of the world,
and their father thought
as they did.
As for the youngest son,
he was named Boots.
Nobody thought anything of him
except that he was silly,
for he did nothing but sit
poking warm ashes all of the day.

One morning Peter spoke up
and said that he was going
to the town.
"I should like to go
and have a try
at befooling the king," said he.

His father did not say *no,*
for if anybody was wise enough
to befool the king,
Peter was the lad.

So, after Peter had eaten
a good breakfast,
off he set for the town,
right foot foremost.
After a while
he came to the king's house
and—rap! tap! tap!—
he knocked at the door.
*Well, what did he want?*
Oh! he would only like
to have a try
at befooling the king.
*Very good;*
*he should have his try.*
He was not the first one
who had been there that morning,
early as it was.
So Peter was shown in
to the king.

165

"Oh, look!" said he,
"yonder are three black geese
   out in the courtyard!"

But no,
   the king was not to be fooled
   so easily as all that.
"One goose is enough
   to look at at a time," said he;
"take him away
   and give him a whipping!"
And so they did,
   and Peter went home
   bleating like a sheep.

One day Paul spoke up.
"I should like to go
   and have a try
   at befooling the king," said he.

Well,
his father did not say *no,*
for, after all,
Paul was the more clever of the two.
So off Paul went
as merrily as a duck
in the rain.

By and by he came to the castle,
and then he, too,
was brought before the king
just as Peter had been.

"Oh, look!" said he,
"yonder is a crow
   sitting in the tree
   with three white stripes
   on his back!"

But the king was not so silly
as to be fooled in that way.
"Here is a Jack," said he,
"who will soon have more stripes
on his back
than he will like.
Take him away
and give him his whipping!"
Then it was done
as the king had said,
and Paul went away home
bawling like a calf.

One day up spoke Boots.
"I should like to go
and have a try
at befooling the king, too,"
said he.

At this
they all stared and sniggered.
*What! He go*
*where his clever brothers*
*had failed,*
*and had nothing to show*
*for the trying*
*but a good beating?*
*What had come over the lout?*
*Here was a pretty business,*
*to be sure!*
That was what they all said.

But all of this rolled away from Boots
like water from a duck's back.

No matter,
he would like to go
and have a try
like the others.
So he begged and begged
until his father was glad
to let him go
to be rid of his teasing,
if nothing else.
Then Boots asked
if he might have
the old tattered hat
that hung back of the chimney.

*Oh, yes,*
*he might have that*
*if he wanted it,*
*for nobody with good wits*
*was likely to wear such a thing.*
So Boots took the hat,
and after he had brushed the ashes
from his shoes,
set off for the town,
whistling as he went.

The first body whom he met
was an old woman
with a great load
of earthenware pots and crocks
on her shoulders.

"Good-day, mother," said Boots.
"Good-day, son," said she.

"What will you take
  for all of your pots and crocks?"
  said Boots.

"Three shillings," said she.

"I will give you five shillings
  if you will come and stand
  in front of the king's house,
  and do thus and so
  when I say this and that,"
  said Boots.

*Oh, yes!*
*She would do that*
*willingly enough.*

So Boots and the old woman
went on together,
and presently came
to the king's house.
When they had come there,
Boots sat down
in front of the door
and began bawling as loud as he could—
"No, I will not!
I will not do it, I say!
No, I will not do it!"

So he kept on,
bawling louder and louder
until he made such a noise
that, at last,
the king himself came out
to see what all the hubbub was about.
But when Boots saw him,
he only bawled out louder than ever.

"No, I will not!
I will not do it, I say!"

"Stop! Stop!" cried the king.
"What is all this about?"

"Why," said Boots,
"everybody wants to buy my cap,
but I will not sell it!
I will not do it, I say!"

"But why should anybody
want to buy
such a cap as that?" said the king.

"Because," said Boots,
"it is a fooling cap
and the only one
in all of the world."

"A fooling cap!" said the king,
for he did not like to hear
of such a cap as that
coming into the town.
"Hum-m-m!
I should like to see you
fool somebody with it.
Could you fool that old body yonder
with the pots and crocks?"

"Oh, yes!
That is easily enough done,"
said Boots, and without more ado,
he took off his tattered cap
and blew into it.
Then he put it on his head again
and bawled out,
"Break pots! Break pots!"

No sooner had he spoken these words
than the old woman jumped up
and began breaking and smashing
her pots and crocks
as though she had gone crazy.
(That is what Boots
had paid her five shillings
for doing,
but of it the king knew nothing.)

"Hui!" said the king to himself,
"I must buy that hat
  from the fellow
  or he will befool me
  for sure and certain."

Then he began talking to Boots
as sweetly as though
he had honey in his mouth.
Perhaps Boots would sell
the hat to him?

*Oh, no!*
*Boots could not think of*
*such a thing*
*as selling his fooling cap.*

*Come, come;*
*the king wanted that hat,*
*and sooner than miss buying it,*
*he would give*
*a whole bag of gold money for it.*

At this Boots looked up
and looked down,
scratching his head.
*Well, he supposed he would have*
*to sell the hat some time,*
*and the king*
*might as well have it*
*as anybody else.*
*But for all that*
*he did not like parting with it.*

So the king gave Boots
the bag of gold,
and Boots gave the king
the old tattered hat,
and then he went his way.

After Boots had gone,
the king blew into the hat
and blew into the hat,
but though he blew enough
breath into it
to sail a big ship,
he did not befool
so much as a single titmouse.
Then, at last, he began to see
that the fooling cap was good
on nobody else's head
but Boots';
and he was none too pleased at that,
you may be sure.

As for Boots,
with his bag of gold
he bought the finest clothes
that were to be had in the town,
and when the next morning had come,
he started away
bright and early
for the king's house.

"I have come," said he,
"to be invited
to the party,
if you please."

At this
the king hemmed and hawed
and scratched his head.
*Yes, Boots had befooled him*
*sure enough,*
*but, after all,*
*he could not be sure*
*of the fooling cap.*
*Still,*
*he would give Boots*
*another chance.*
*Now there was the high-councillor,*
*who was the wisest man*
*in all of the world.*
*Did Boots think*
*that he could fool him also?*

171

*Oh, yes!*
*Boots thought*
*that it might be done.*

*Very well;*
*if he could befool the high-councillor*
*so as to bring him*
*to the castle*
*the next morning*
*against his will,*
*Boots should have won*
*the bargain to fool the king;*
*if he did not do so,*
*he should have his beating.*

Then Boots went away
and the king thought
that he was rid of him now
for good and all.

As for the high-councillor,
he was not pleased
with the matter at all,
for he did not like the thought
of being fooled
by a clever rogue,
and taken here and there
against his will.

So when he had come home,
he armed all of his servants
with blunderbusses,
and then waited
to give Boots a *welcome*
when he should come.

But Boots was not going to fall
into any such trap as that!
No indeed! Not he!

The next morning he went quietly
and bought a fine large meal-sack.
Then he put a wig
over his beautiful hair,
so that no one might know him.

After that
he went to the place
where the high-councillor lived,
and when he had come there,
he crawled inside the sack
and lay just beside
the door of the house.
By and by
came one of the maidservants
to the door,
and there lay
the great meal-sack
with somebody in it.

"Ach!" cried she,
"who is there?"

But Boots only said, "Sh-h-h!"

Then the serving maid
went back into the house
and told the high-councillor
that one lay outside
in a great meal-sack
and that all that he said was,
"Sh-h-h-h-h."
So the councillor went himself
to see what it was all about.

"What do you want here?" said he.

"Sh-h-h-h-h!" said Boots,
"I am not to be talked to now.
This is a wisdom sack,
and I am learning wisdom
as fast as a drake
can eat peas."

"And what wisdom have you learned?"
said the councillor.

*Oh! Boots had learned wisdom
about everything in the world.
He had learned*

*that the clever scamp*
*who had fooled the king yesterday*
*was coming*
*with seventeen tall men*
*to take the high-councillor,*
*willy-nilly,*
*to the castle that morning.*

When the high-councillor
heard this,
he fell to trembling
till his teeth rattled
in his head.

"And have you learned
how I can get the better
of this clever scamp?"
said he.

*Oh yes!*
*Boots had learned that*
*easily enough.*

*So, good!*
*Then if the wise man in the sack*
*would tell the high-councillor*
*how to escape the clever rogue,*
*the high-councillor*
*would give the wise man*
*twenty shillings.*

*But no,*
*that was not to be done;*
*wisdom was not bought so cheaply*
*as the high councillor*
*seemed to think.*

*Well,*
*the councillor would give him*
*a hundred shillings, then.*
*That was good!*
*A hundred shillings*
*was a hundred shillings.*
*If the councillor*

*would give him that much,*
*he might get into the sack*
*himself,*
*and then he could learn*
*all the wisdom that he wanted,*
*and more besides.*

So Boots crawled out of the sack,
and the councillor
paid his hundred shillings
and crawled in.
As soon as he was in
all snug and safe,
Boots drew
the mouth of the sack together
and tied it tightly.
Then he flung sack,
councillor and all,
over his shoulder
and started away to the king's house,
and anybody who met them
could see with half an eye
that the councillor was going
against his will.

When Boots came
to the king's castle,
he laid the councillor down
in the goose-house,
and then he went to the king.

When the king saw Boots again,
he bit his lips
with vexation.

"Well," said he,
"have you fooled the councillor?"

"Oh, yes!" said Boots,
"I have done that."

*And where was the councillor now?*

*Oh, Boots had just left him
down in the goose-house.
He was tied up
safe and sound
in a sack
waiting*

*till the king
should send for him.*

So the councillor was sent for,
and when he came,
the king saw at once
that he had been brought
against his will.

"And now
may I come to the party?"
said Boots.

But the king was not willing
to invite him yet;
*no! no!*

177

Boots must not go so fast.
There was more to be done yet.
If he would come
tomorrow morning,
he might join the princess' party
and be welcome,
if he could pick her out
from among fourscore other maids
just like her;
did he think
that he could do that?

Oh, yes!
Boots thought
that might be easy enough to do.

So, good!
Then come tomorrow;
but he must understand
that if he failed,
he should have a good whipping
and be sent packing
from the town.

So off went Boots,
and the king thought
that he was rid of him now,
for he had never seen the princess,
and how could he pick her out
from eighty others?

But Boots was not going
to give up so easily
as all that!
*No, not he!*

He made a little box,
and then he hunted up and down
until he had caught a live mouse
to put into it.

When the next morning came,
he started away
to the king's house,
taking his mouse along with him
in the box.
There was the king,
standing in the doorway,
looking out into the street.
When he saw Boots
coming towards him
he made a wry face.

"What!" said he,
"are you back again?"

*Oh, yes!*
*Boots was back again.*
*And now*
*if the princess was ready,*
*he would like*
*to go and find her,*
*for lost time*
*was not be gathered again*
*like fallen apples.*

So off they marched
to a great room,
and there stood
eighty-and-one maidens,
all as much alike
as peas in the same dish.
Boots looked here and there,
but even if he had known
the princess,
he could not have told her
from the others.
But he was ready
for all that.
Before anyone knew
what he was about,
he opened the box,
and out ran the little mouse
among them all.
Then what a screaming
and a hubbub
there was.
Many looked as though
they would have liked to swoon,
but only one of them did so.

As soon as the others
saw what had happened,
they forgot all about the mouse
and ran to her
and fell to fanning her
and slapping her hands
and chafing her temples.

"This is the princess,"
said Boots.

And so it was.

After that
the king could think
of nothing more
to set Boots to do.
So he let him
meet the princess
as he had promised,
and as you can guess,
Boots and the princess fell in love
and were married.

That is all
of this story.
Only this:
*It is not always*
*the silliest one*
*that sits kicking his feet*
*in the ashes at home.*

As wet as a —as dry as a bone;

As live as a bird—as dead as a stone;

As plump as a partridge—as poor as a rat;

As strong as a —as weak as a ;

As hard as a flint—as soft as a mole;

As white as a lily—as black as a coal;

As plain as a staff—as rough as a ;

As tight as a —as free as the air;

As heavy as lead—as light as a ;

As steady as time—as uncertain as weather;

As hot as an oven—as cold as a ;

As gay as a lark—as sick as a ;

As savage as tigers—as mild as a dove;

As stiff as a poker—as limp as a ;

As blind as a bat—as deaf as a post;

As cool as a —as warm as toast;

As blunt as a —as sharp as an awl;

As flat as a flounder—as round as a ;

As brittle as glass—as tough as gristle;

As neat as a pin—as clean as a ;

As red as a —as square as a box;

As bold as a thief—as sly as a .

anonymous                                    pictures by Betty Fraser

COMPARISONS

182

183

# Alligator on the Escalator

THROUGH THE DEPARTMENT STORE THERE SLITHERED AN ALLIGATOR. WHEN HE CAME TO THE ESCALATOR, HE STEPPED UPON THE TRACK WITH GREAT

DEXTERITY; HIS TAIL DRAPED OVER THE RAILING, AND HE CLICKED HIS TEETH

IN GLEE; "YO, I'M OFF ON THE ESCALATOR,
EXCITED AS I CAN BE!
IT'S A *MOVING* EXPERIENCE,
AS YOU CAN PLAINLY SEE.
ON THE MOVING STAIR I GO ANYWHERE,
I RISE TO THE TOP,
PAST OUTERWEAR, INNERWEAR,
DINNERWARE, THINNERWEAR—
THEN DOWN TO THE BASEMENT WITH BARGAINS GALORE, THEN BACK ON THE TRACK TO THE TOP ONCE MORE!
OH, I MAY RIDE THE ESCALATOR
UNTIL CLOSING TIME OR LATER,
SO TELL THE TELEPHONE OPERATOR
TO CALL MRS. ALBERT Q. ALLIGATOR
AND TELL HER TO TAKE A HOT MUD BATH
AND NOT TO WAIT UP FOR ME!"

by Eve Merriam

pictures by Kelly Oechsli

# Ten Billion, Ten Mil...

10, 010, 010, 010
Is a number so grand
You say it again:
10, 010, 010, 010!

10, 010, 010, 010
Is a number so superly fine,
But I'd like to point out it's only one more than—
10, 010, 010, 009!

a verse by Phil Keils

Crocodile

# Inside the

## Ten Thousand, Ten

an old song

She sailed away
on a happy summer day
on the back of a crocodile;
"You see," said she,
"he's as tame as he can be,
I'll ride him down the Nile."
The croc winked his eye
as he bade them all goodbye,
wearing a happy smile;

at the end of the ride
the lady was inside
of the smile on the crocodile.

It is a cold winter in northern
British Columbia. At the Fehr farm
snow has covered the ground
since early November and it will
not melt until May.

One clear night in February the
temperature drops to forty degrees
below zero and the northern lights
flash across the sky. Mary Fehr
gets out of bed and goes to the
window to watch and listen. She
hears a crackling sound and smiles,
excited. Mary likes to pretend
that if she hears the music of the
lights, the next day will bring
something special.

# Mary of Mile 18

story and pictures by Ann Blades

The next morning Mary Fehr wakes up happy. At first she can't think why. Then she remembers, and wonders what the day will bring. She pulls on her boots, hat, heavy coat and mitts, and walks to the henhouse to feed the chickens.

One winter day is so much like the next. What could happen? Her mother is expecting a new baby, but it is not supposed to arrive for another month.

Mary feeds the chickens and starts
back. Seeing the house in front
of her reminds her of another special
day, the day her father finished
building it. He was so proud. When
the family first moved to the farm,
they lived in the shack where the
grain is now kept. Before that they
lived in town, but Mary does not
remember so far back.

Mary's mother has told her of the
comforts of town: water taps,
electricity, telephones, and television.
Here, water is brought into the
house a pail at a time; the sink drains
into another pail which is carried
outside and emptied. The bathroom is
an outhouse and the bathtub is a
big bucket. The family has a transistor
radio to listen to, but Mrs. Fehr gets
lonely sometimes.

The closest neighbors are the Bergens,
and their farm is two miles away.

Mary sees her father near the barn.
The caterpillar was damaged
yesterday, and he is trying to fix it.
Every winter day when it does not
snow, Mr. Fehr likes to clear a little
more land. He uses the cat to
push the trees down and into piles.

When summer comes all the family
will pick roots, tearing them out
of the earth with their hands so that
the land can be planted.

"When we clear most of this land,
the Government will give us the
deed to it," her father explained.
"This is why we have moved north;
so that we can have our own farm
and live our own way."

Before he comes in for breakfast,
Mr. Fehr puts a propane torch
under the truck to warm the engine.
It will take an hour to warm
because last night was so cold.

Usually Mary likes this time just
before they set out for school.
Mr. Fehr is playing with little Eva.
Isaac and Jake are looking at
a book from the class library. This
morning Sarah tries to get Mary
to crayon with her, but Mary can't
keep her mind on it. What could
happen today? She is anxious to get
to school.

Mrs. Fehr serves breakfast. After the
new baby comes, the girls will
help even more than now. They will
do dishes, cook meals, make beds,
and scrub floors. But they won't mind.
A new baby is so exciting.

The radio is on. The weather report is:
"Snow this afternoon. Clearing and
colder towards evening."

Mr. Fehr goes out first and starts
the engine. He lets it run for a
while, then honks the horn. Mary,
Sarah, Jake, and Isaac come out and
crowd into the seat beside him.
It is a tight squeeze, but it is also nice
and warm.

Today the teacher, Mrs. Burns,
has turned the oil heater on full, but
the room is still so cold that the
children sitting beside the windows
keep their coats on and edge closer
to the heater. At noontime Sarah
watches the class while Mrs. Burns
goes to the back to have her lunch.
At three o'clock Mary helps dress the
smaller children. She ties their
scarves over their heads and across
their faces to protect them from
the cold.

Mary sighs as she pulls on her own
overshoes. School is over for the day
and still nothing special has happened.

In the truck on the way home,
Mr. Fehr listens to the children talk
about school but does not talk
himself. He is watching the road
carefully. Snow is drifting and it
is hard to see.

Just as they near their farm, another
truck looms out of the blowing
snow. Mr. Fehr steers quickly to the
right to avoid an accident and
his back wheels slide into the ditch.

As Mary watches her father jack up
the truck and put chains on the rear
tires, she thinks, "I hope *that's*
not the special thing."

Then, farther up the road to the
house, Mary sees something in the
snow and cries: "Look, a puppy."
She runs to him, kneels down, and
the puppy licks her mitt.

Mary carries the pup to the truck.
"Please, father, can I keep him?"

Mr. Fehr shakes his head. "You
know the rules. Our animals must
work for us or give us food."

Mary protests: "A dog can help . . ."

Mr. Fehr interrupts: "That isn't a
regular dog. He's part wolf,
and wolf-pups are useless. Take him
into the woods and leave him.
Come on the rest of you. Chores."

Sadly Mary goes off with the pup
while the others go about their jobs.
Jake goes to the woodpile, takes
an axe, splits logs, and carries them,
an armful at a time, into the
house. Both the wood stove that
Mrs. Fehr uses for cooking and
the barrel heater that warms the house
take a lot of wood. Sometimes even
when both are going, the house is
chilly.

The pup snuggles in Mary's arms
as she carries him into the woods.
How she wishes she could keep him!
"I would call you Wolf," she says.

It has stopped snowing, but the
path is covered over and the trees
seem to grow closer and closer
together. If she goes too far from
the road, she might not be able
to find her way back. She puts the
pup down to see what will happen.
He runs around, excited, sniffing
at the trees. She turns and walks
away. He does not follow.

"That was something special
alright," Mary thinks, as she walks
home, "but it didn't last for long."

Near the house Isaac passes her
on their horse, Mouse. A few years
ago Isaac and Jake rode Mouse
to school and kept her in the barn
behind the schoolhouse. But now
Mouse has to wait until Isaac gets
home to go for a run.

The house smells of fresh-baked
bread as Mary enters. Her mother
looks up from the stove.

"Where have you been, Mary?
Sarah was waiting for you. I'm almost
out of water."

Silently Mary bends down, takes
two empty buckets standing near the
door and goes out.

Sarah has already filled her
buckets with snow. Mary does the
same and the two girls carry the
snow into the house and dump it
into a big barrel. They wait for
it to melt, then go out for more snow.

From the barrel comes all the water
for drinking, cooking, and washing.
Tomorrow Mrs. Fehr will wash clothes
and Sarah will stay home to help,
so the barrel must be full tonight. In
spring and summer, it is much
easier. A barrel catches rain water
from the roof, and the river is
unfrozen. But in winter all the water
comes from snow. When the snow
is dry and powdery like today, it takes
many trips to fill the barrel.

Each time Mary goes out, she looks
toward the woods. Her father comes
out of the barn where he has been
feeding the pigs and goes into the
house. Isaac returns with Mouse. The
pup is nowhere in sight.

The coal oil lamp is lit and Mary
sits at the table staring at her
reader. Mrs. Fehr is making supper.
Mr. Fehr is cleaning his gun. The
radio says another cold night, and
Mary thinks about the pup.

Suddenly there is a sound outside
the door, a low whimper. Mr. Fehr
goes to the door and opens it. Mary
cries: "It's little Wolf," and
rushes to take the pup in her arms.

Mr. Fehr is angry. "Why are you
encouraging him to stay around? Get
your coat on and get rid of him so
that he doesn't come back."

This time Mary walks nearly two
miles to the Bergen farm. "Perhaps
Mr. Bergen will let his children
keep you," she says, putting Wolf
down near the door. "Then I can see
you sometimes."

As she runs home in the cold night
her toes and fingertips sting and the
air burns her throat.

The family is at the supper table
when she gets back. Her mother looks
up, says: "We have your favorite
supper tonight, Mary. Moose steak."

"I don't want to eat, mother."

Mrs. Fehr starts to object, but
Mr. Fehr stops her: "Let the girl go to
bed without eating if she wants to."
His voice is still angry. "She should
not have asked to keep the animal.
She knows the rules."

Mary gets into bed and buries her
head in her pillow. "Why should he
be so angry?" she wonders. Then
she remembers last fall when Jake
and Isaac begged their father
for a gun of their own. He refused
and got angry then, too. Her mother
explained: "Your father gives you
everything he can. When you ask for
more, it hurts him to refuse. That
is why he gets angry."

Mary lies thinking about this until
she falls asleep.

That night when everyone in the
Fehr house is asleep, another
kind of animal, a coyote, comes out
of the woods. He sniffs at all
the buildings, then stops at the
henhouse. Silently he paws at
the rope that holds the door shut,
and the rope comes loose. The
coyote pushes the door to enter the
henhouse and get at the chickens.

Suddenly, a shrill screech goes up
in the night.

Everyone in the Fehr house wakes up.
Mr. Fehr throws his clothes on
quickly, grabs his gun and goes out.

The rest of the family get up and
crowd around the window to see
what is happening. All except Mary.
She hears Isaac say, "It's just
a coyote," and she tries to go back
to sleep, so that she won't have
to think about little Wolf out in
the woods.

Mr. Fehr sees the coyote in the
bright light from the snow. He aims
his gun and fires.

His first shot misses. The coyote
turns, snarling, then quickly runs
behind the henhouse. Mr. Fehr fires
again, but the coyote takes off and
disappears over the hill.

Mr. Fehr goes to the henhouse,
looks inside to make sure the chickens
are alright. Then he carefully ties
the door tight. He is about to return to
the house when he sees something
at his feet.

It is the wolf-pup wagging his tail.

"So it was you who warned us,"
Mr. Fehr says. He bends down,
takes the puppy in his hands, and
looks at him. "Tough little fellow,
aren't you? Not afraid of cold or
coyotes. Maybe you will earn your
keep after all."

He carries the pup into the house.
Mrs. Fehr has lit the oil lamp and
everyone is waiting for him, except
Mary.

The children get excited when they
see the wolf-pup. Mr. Fehr puts
his finger to his lips as a sign for
them to be silent. He goes to the
bedroom.

Mary looks up as her father comes into the bedroom. He puts the wolf-pup down on the bed. "This little fellow would like to get warm," he says.

Mary can hardly believe she is not dreaming as she takes little Wolf in her arms. "Can I keep him?" she asks.

"I suppose you can," her father answers gruffly.

In the doorway of the bedroom, Isaac and Jake and Sarah and Mrs. Fehr, holding Eva in her arms, are all standing watching and smiling.

# PACHYCEPHALOSAURUS
## (pak-i-sef-a-lo-saw-rus)

Among the later dinosaurs
  Though not the largest, strongest,
PACHYCEPHALOSAURUS had
  The name that was the longest.

Yet he had more than syllables,
  As you may well suppose.
He had great knobs upon his cheeks
  And spikes upon his nose.

Ten inches thick, atop his head,
  A bump of bone projected.
By this his brain, though hardly worth
  Protecting, was protected.

No claw or tooth, no tree that fell
  Upon his head kerwhacky,
Could crack or crease or jar or scar
  That stony part of Paky.

And so he nibbled plants in peace
  And lived untroubled days.
Sometimes, in fact, as Paky proved,
  To be a bonehead pays.

by Richard Armour
illustration by Bob Shein